I Can L[...]
MEGA MATHS
Age 5-7

100 stickers

Activities by Michael Tonge and Lindsay Hancock

Illustrated by Pip Adams, Craig Cameron, Kelly Dooley and John Haslam

EGMONT
We bring stories to life

First published in Great Britain in 2004 by Egmont UK Limited
239 Kensington High Street, London W8 6SA
Published in this edition in 2005

© 2008 Egmont UK Limited

ISBN 978 1 4052 2014 9

5 7 9 10 8 6 4

Printed in Italy

Contents

Contents

100
Stickers

Mega Maths 5–7 offers lots of practice in numeracy skills as described in the guidelines for the National Numeracy Strategy. The book reflects the content of the National Curriculum in England and Wales and the 5–14 Maths programme in Scotland.

This book covers the following areas, which reflect the five strands in the National Numeracy Strategy:

1. Calculations
2. Numbers and the number system
3. Solving problems
4. Handling data
5. Measure, shape and space

This book is aimed at children aged 5–7, so the levels of the exercises are progressively more difficult. As children move up from Reception to Year 1 and then to Year 2, the topics under each strand increase.

Some topics may seem ambitious, but these are aimed at 7-year-olds or those children who require and can cope with more challenging questions.

We recommend that your child works through the book in the given order. If he or she starts to struggle with any of the pages, skip these questions and return to them when he or she is feeling more confident. Repetition and practice will help build skills and confidence.

Answers appear at the end of each section, so that either you or your child can check and mark the work. After each answer section is a list of useful words and a checklist, which will help you and your child to record progress made.

Your child can add the 100 fun stickers to the pages of the book, or use them to decorate pencil cases, posters or other items.

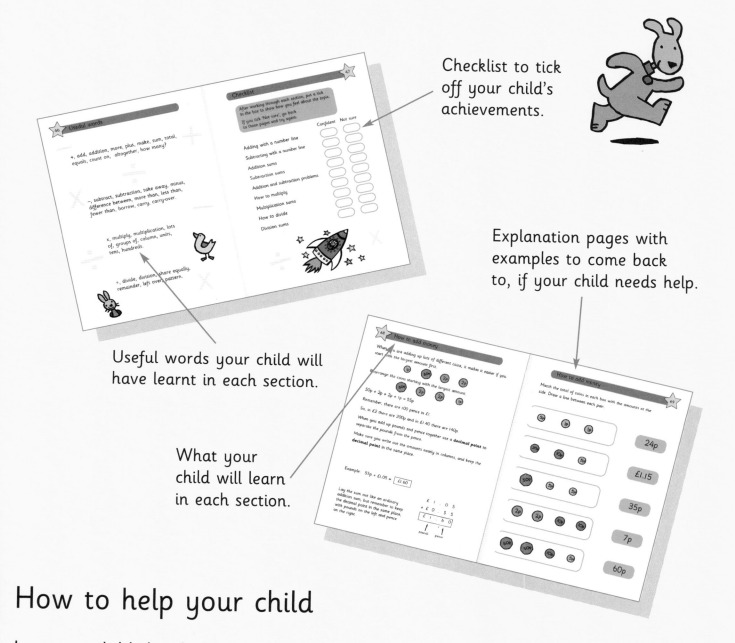

Checklist to tick off your child's achievements.

Explanation pages with examples to come back to, if your child needs help.

Useful words your child will have learnt in each section.

What your child will learn in each section.

How to help your child

Let your child decide how long he or she wants to work on the book. The book is designed for your child to start and stop any time he or she wishes. Give lots of encouragement and praise for effort.

Instructions are written clearly and simply, but you may need to look through the activities and explain what your child is being asked to do. If your child has problems with a type of activity, talk about it together and try to help. You may want to discuss it with your child's class teacher.

To add with a number line start with the larger number and **count on** the smaller number in steps.

When you start counting the steps, count on from the number **after** the starting number.

Example: 6 + 4 = 10

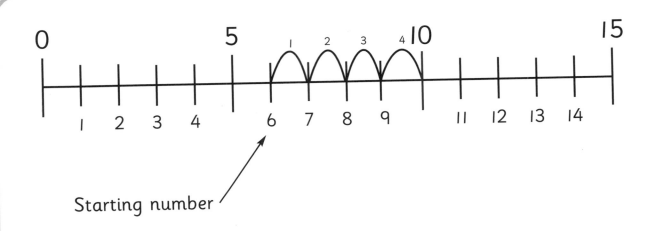

Starting number

A faster way of working out the answer is to move across the number line in **big** steps. Try counting on in 2s.

Example: 32 + 6 = 38

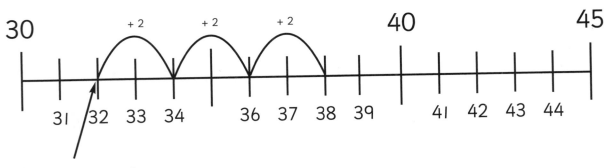

Starting number

Write in the missing numbers.
Use the number line to help you.

0   5   10   15   20   25
1 2 3 4   6 7 8 9   11 12 13 14   16 17 18 19   21 22 23 24

15 + 3 =

17 + 5 =

20 + 2 =

21 + 4 =

9 + 10 =

Write the answer in words.

ten **plus** one **equals**

two **plus** six **equals**

nine **plus** eight **equals**

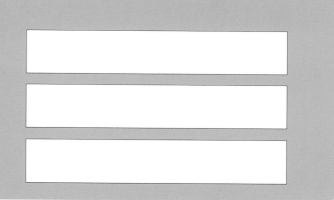

Addition with a number line

Write in the missing numbers.
Use the number line to help you.

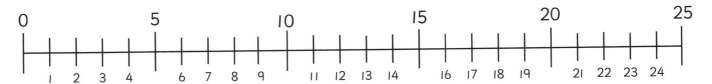

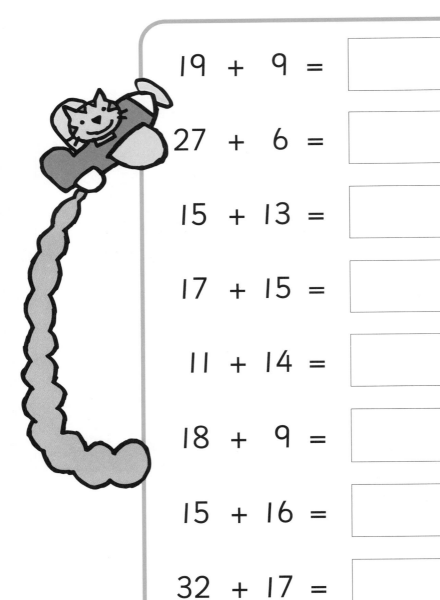

19 + 9 =

27 + 6 =

15 + 13 =

17 + 15 =

11 + 14 =

18 + 9 =

15 + 16 =

32 + 17 =

Write in the missing numbers.
Use the number line to help you.

8 + 9 + 7 =

15 + 10 + 5 =

11 + 13 + 2 =

22 + 4 + 6 =

40 + 4 + 5 =

35 + 12 + 1 =

5 + 20 + 13 =

19 + 9 + 3 =

When you are doing subtraction sums start with the larger number and **count back** the number of steps shown by the smaller number.

Example: 15 − 7 = 8

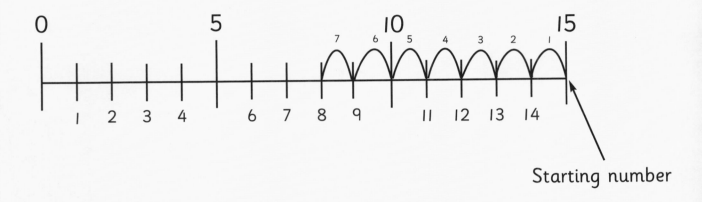

Starting number

If the number that you are taking away is a big number it makes it easier to **leap** backwards rather than step.

Example: 43 − 17 = 26

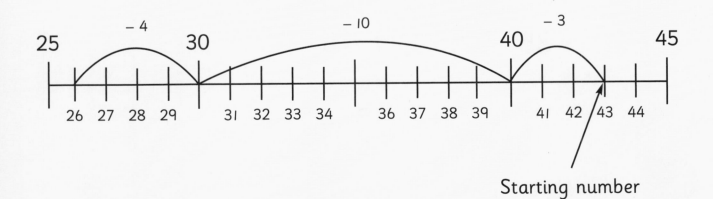

Starting number

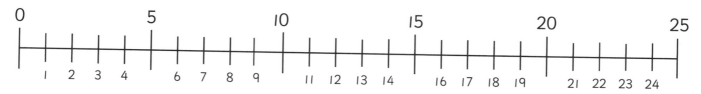
Write in the missing numbers.
Use the number line to help you.

0   5   10   15   20   25
1 2 3 4   6 7 8 9   11 12 13 14   16 17 18 19   21 22 23 24

20 – 6 =

24 – 11 =

17 – 6 =

14 – 4 =

22 – 21 =

12 – 1 =

18 – 12 =

9 – 4 =

Write in the missing numbers.
Use the number line to help you.

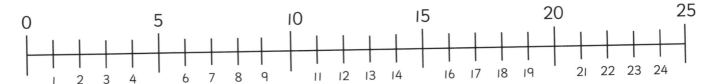

$10 - 4 =$ ⬚

$15 - 3 =$ ⬚

$17 - 8 =$ ⬚

$12 - 6 =$ ⬚

$20 - 11 =$ ⬚

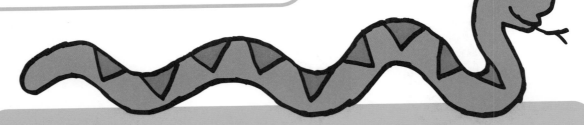

Write the answer in words.

nine **take away** three **equals** ⬚

eleven **take away** six **equals** ⬚

twelve **take away** seven **equals** ⬚

Write in the missing numbers.
Use the number line to help you.

```
    30        35        40        45        50
|  |  |  |  |  |  |  |  |  |  |  |  |  |  |  |  |  |  |  |  |  |  |  |
26 27 28 29  31 32 33 34  36 37 38 39  41 42 43 44  46 47 48 49
```

$$50 - 5 - 5 = \boxed{}$$

$$40 - 3 - 6 = \boxed{}$$

$$25 - 12 - 2 = \boxed{}$$

$$31 - 4 - 3 = \boxed{}$$

$$15 - 5 - 1 = \boxed{}$$

$$46 - 11 - 3 = \boxed{}$$

$$26 - 7 - 9 = \boxed{}$$

$$38 - 6 - 8 = \boxed{}$$

When the missing numbers are in the **middle** of the sum, it will help if you turn the sum around. You can make an addition a subtraction, or a subtraction an addition!

Example: 20 − ☐ = 8

Turn the sum around from a subtraction sum to make it an addition sum.

8 + ☐ = 20

Now use the number line and count the steps.

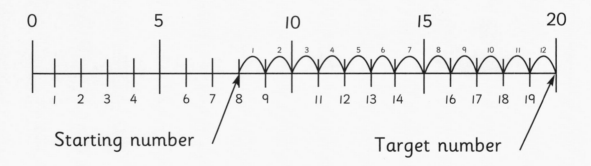

Starting number   Target number

It takes 12 steps!

Now you can fill in the sums:

8 + 12 = 20   is the same as   20 − 12 = 8

See how easy it is!

Write in the missing numbers.
Use the number line to help you.

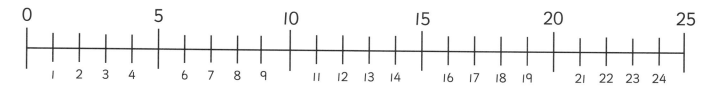

0   5   10   15   20   25

1 2 3 4   6 7 8 9   11 12 13 14   16 17 18 19   21 22 23 24

0 + ☐ = 20

15 + ☐ = 18

17 − ☐ = 12

12 + ☐ = 20

20 − ☐ = 11

14 + ☐ = 19

Match the number 15 to three of these boxes.

10 + 5

17 − 3

11 + 7

15

18 − 6

9 + 6

20 − 5

13 − 9

Addition sums can be written in lots of different ways.

Here are some 'adding' words that you might come across:

add   **plus**   **sum**   **and**   **total**   **altogether**

Example:

If 3 girls and 4 boys go to the park, how many children go altogether?

The important word is **altogether**; it means you must add up **all** the numbers given in the question. The answer to this example is 7.

Set out your sums neatly and write your answers in tidy columns.

Start with the units, add them up, then write the answer directly underneath.

Now do the same with the numbers in the tens column.

Example:

$$
\begin{array}{cc}
\text{T} & \text{U} \\
3 & 7 \\
+1 & 2 \\
\hline
4 & 9 \\
\end{array}
$$

3 + 1 = 4   7 + 2 = 9

Work out these sums and problems.

23	32	56	46
+ 16	+ 15	+ 23	+ 31

**Sedgley Brown
Junior School**

Class 3 – 26 pupils
Class 4 – 31 pupils
Class 5 – 32 pupils
Class 6 – 22 pupils

If classes 3 and 4 go on a trip to the zoo,
how many children go altogether?

What is the total number of children
in classes 5 and 6?

If every class except class 6 goes into
assembly, how many children are in assembly?

Sometimes when you add up the numbers in an addition sum, the answer has two digits.

When this happens you must **carry** the first digit (the tens) below the line under the tens column.

Example:

$$4 + 3 + 1 = 8 \left\{ \begin{array}{cc} 4 & 9 \\ + 3 & 7 \end{array} \right\} \quad 9 + 7 = 16$$

8	6

1

This goes here

The trick is to line up the numbers in **columns**.
Then it is clear to see what you are adding up.

This works when adding with hundreds too.

Example:

$$1 + 1 + 1 = 3 \left\{ \begin{array}{ccc} 1 & 8 & 2 \\ + 1 & 2 & 4 \end{array} \right\} \begin{array}{l} 2 + 4 = 6 \\ 8 + 2 = 10 \end{array}$$

3	0	6

1

This goes here

Work out these sums and problems.

38	27	59	159
+ 19	+ 18	+ 53	+ 264

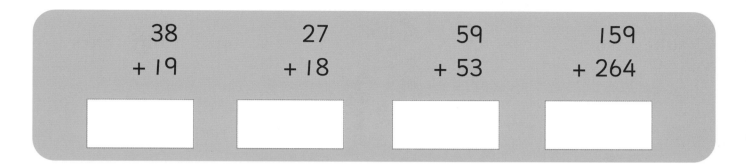

Airfun Airlines Passenger List

Paris 234   London 125   Madrid 97

Moscow 104   New York 124

How many passengers altogether are
going to Moscow and New York?

How many passengers altogether are
flying to London and Paris?

How many passengers altogether are on
flights going to London, Paris and Madrid?

Subtraction sums can be written in lots of different ways.

Here are some 'subtracting' words that you might come across:

take away   **subtract**   **more than**   **less than**   **difference**

Example: What is the difference between 20 and 5?

The key word is **difference**, and it means you must take the smaller number away from the larger number (find the difference 'in between' them). The answer to this example is 15.

Set out subtraction sums in the same way you did the addition sums on page 16.

Start with the units, take the bottom number away from the top number, then write the answer directly underneath.

Now do the same with the numbers in the tens column.

Example:

$$
4 - 1 = 3 \left\{ \begin{array}{cc} \textbf{T} & \textbf{U} \\ 4 & 5 \\ -1 & 2 \end{array} \right\} 5 - 2 = 3
$$

$$
\boxed{\begin{array}{cc} 3 & 3 \end{array}}
$$

Solve these sums and problems.

68	29	39	71	18
− 23	− 26	− 13	− 21	− 15

Second Hand Shop   OPEN

9p   CAKES   47p   Animal Farm Box Set

12p   59p

How much more is the torch than the doll?

☐ − ☐ = ☐

What is the difference in price between the most expensive item and the cheapest item?

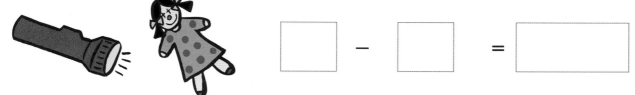

☐ − ☐ = ☐

How much less is the doll than the toy farm?

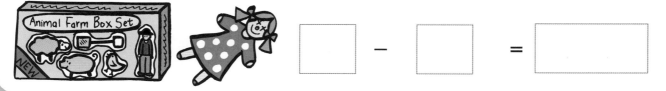

☐ − ☐ = ☐

Sometimes you may come across problems when you take away numbers in columns.

Example:

$$\begin{array}{cc} \mathbf{T} & \mathbf{U} \\ 4 & 2 \\ -\ 2 & 7 \end{array}$$

} 7 is more than 2

All you need to do is **borrow** a ten from the tens column.

Cross one of the tens out to show that you have borrowed it, then add it to the units column:

$$\begin{array}{cc} \mathbf{T} & \mathbf{U} \\ ^3\cancel{4} & ^12 \\ -\ 2 & 7 \\ \hline & 5 \end{array}$$

} 12 − 7 = 5

Now subtract the tens in the tens column in the usual way:

$$3 - 2 = 1 \quad \begin{cases} \mathbf{T} & \mathbf{U} \\ ^3\cancel{4} & ^12 \\ -\ 2 & 7 \end{cases}$$

$$\begin{array}{cc} 1 & 5 \end{array}$$

Solve these sums and problems.

72	23	56	81	12
− 13	− 15	− 17	− 19	− 5

Steve and Sal's Sandwich Sales

Monday 112 Tuesday 123
Wednesday 78 Thursday 79

How many more sandwiches were
sold on Tuesday than on Wednesday?

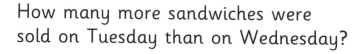 ☐ − ☐ = ☐

What is the difference between
the biggest and smallest number
of sandwiches sold?

 ☐ − ☐ = ☐

How many fewer sandwiches were sold on
Thursday than on Monday?

 ☐ − ☐ = ☐

If Steve and Sal's best sale ever was 200 sandwiches,
how many fewer than this
did they sell on Monday?

 ☐ − ☐ = ☐
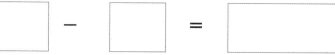

Addition sums can be written in **any** order.

Example: $10 + 5 = 15$ $5 + 10 = 15$

It doesn't matter which number you start with – you always get the **same answer**.

This also works for sums with lots of numbers to be added.

Example : $4 + 2 + 5 + 7 + 3 = 21$

$7 + 2 + 3 + 4 + 5 = 21$

But, subtraction sums **cannot** be written in any order.

Example: $15 - 6 = 9$ $6 - 15 =$ **The answer isn't 9**!

Addition and subtraction sums have a special **relationship** with each other. They are the **opposite** of each other.

Example: $20 - 15 = 5$

If we change the numbers around we can turn it into an addition sum:
        $5 + 15 = 20$

Example: $5 + 7 = 12$

If we change the numbers around we can turn it into a subtraction sum:
        $12 - 7 = 5$

Fill in the missing signs (+ or −) or numbers to make the sums work.
The first one has been done for you.

30 [+] [40] = [70]

45 [ ] [ ] = [57]

90 [ ] [ ] = [140]

70 [ ] [40] = [30]

25 [+] [12] = [ ]

70 [ ] [ ] = [40]

What are the missing numbers here?

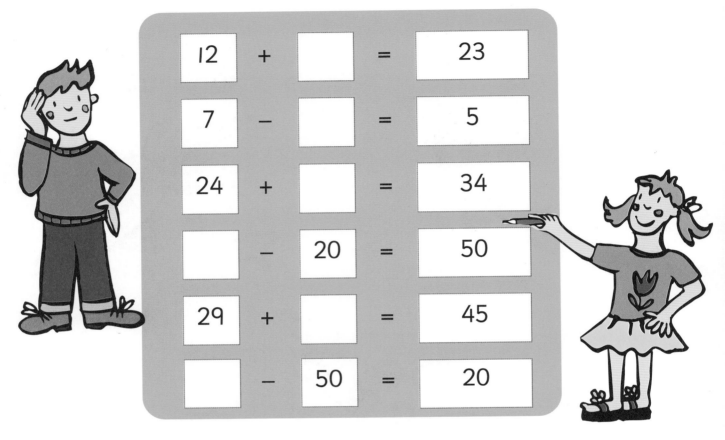

12	+		=	23
7	–		=	5
24	+		=	34
	–	20	=	50
29	+		=	45
	–	50	=	20

Here is a chart showing some of a football league's results.
Complete the chart and use the information to work out who won the league.

Win = 4 points
Draw = 2 points
Loss = 1 point

Team	Won	Drew	Lost	Points
United	4	1	3	21
City	5	2	1	
Flint	3	4	1	
Crewe	4	3	1	
Mold	4		0	24

Winner:

Write the missing numbers to complete the sums.

5	+		= 12
30	−		= 20
	+ 15		= 27
	− 4		= 16
21	+		= 38
35	−		= 15

$5 + \boxed{} = 12$

$30 - \boxed{} = 20$

$\boxed{} + 15 = 27$

$\boxed{} - 4 = 16$

$21 + \boxed{} = 38$

$35 - \boxed{} = 15$

Here is a chart showing how many people went on the rides in a small theme park during one week.

Complete the chart.

	Mon	Tues	Wed	Thurs	Fri	Sat	Sun
Big Dipper	2	5	9	3	2	8	9
Log Flume	1	6	9	2	6	9	7
Rapids	8	11	3	9	6	2	7
Total visitors per day							

On which day did the most people visit the theme park?

3 x 2 = ☐

In the multiplication sum above we are trying to find 3 **lots of** 2.

That's what multiplication is – finding **lots of** numbers.

It makes it easier if we draw pictures to show this:

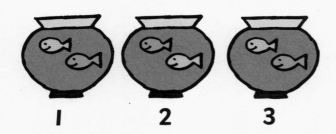

There are 3 **lots** of **groups** of 2 fish.

If we count all the fish we find that there are 6.

So, 3 x 2 = 6

Multiplication is easier if you think of it as lots and lots of addition.

In the sum: 3 x 2 = ☐   all you were doing was adding 2 together 3 times:

2 + 2 + 2 = 6

So multiplication is just quick addition!

Fill in the missing numbers and complete the sums.

2 x [ ] = [ ]

4 x [ ] = [ ]

3 x [ ] = [ ]

4 x [ ] = [ ]

3 x [ ] = [ ]

Multiplication sums can be worked out in **any** order you like.

Example: 2 x 3 = 6   3 x 2 = 6

It doesn't matter which way round you work out the sum – you always end up with the same answer!

So, '2 lots of 3' is the same as '3 lots of 2'.

Look at these pictures to check if this is correct.

3 lots of 2 = 6 squirrels   2 lots of 3 = 6 squirrels

Multiplication patterns are sometimes tricky to spot.
You just need to know what to look for.

Example:
2	4		8	10		14	

There are 3 missing numbers in this pattern.

The numbers that are already there go up in twos.

Let's see if this will work for the numbers next to the gaps.

	+2	+2		+2	+2		+2	
2	4	**6**	8	10	**12**	14	**16**

It works! You've cracked the pattern!

Draw a line to match sums that have the same answer.

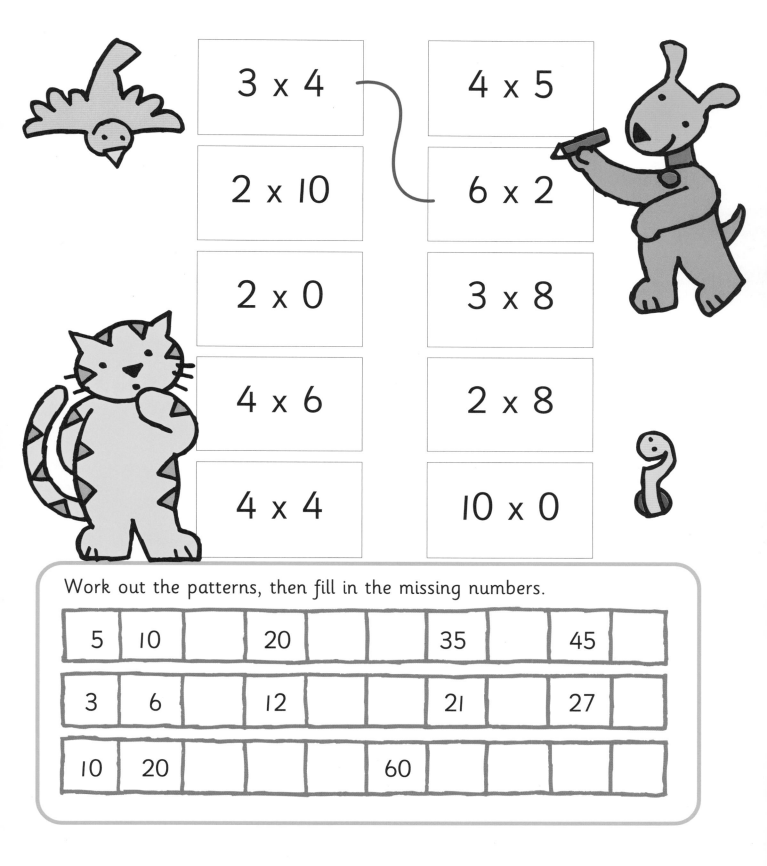

3 x 4	4 x 5
2 x 10	6 x 2
2 x 0	3 x 8
4 x 6	2 x 8
4 x 4	10 x 0

Work out the patterns, then fill in the missing numbers.

5	10		20			35		45	
3	6		12			21		27	
10	20				60				

Multiplication sums need to be worked out in the correct order.

First multiply the bottom number with the **units** of the top number.

Then multiply the bottom number with the **tens** of the top number.

Add any **carry-over** to this number to get your final answer.

Example:

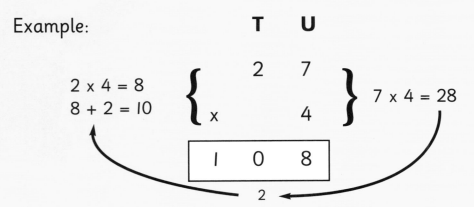

2 x 4 = 8
8 + 2 = 10

T	U
2	7
x	4

7 x 4 = 28

1	0	8

2

Example:

T	U
3	2
x	5

2 x 5 = 10

3 x 5 = 15
15 + 1 = 16

1	6	0

1

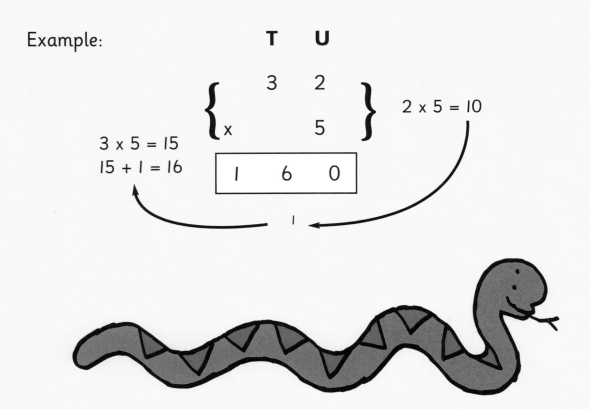

Solve these sums and problems.

23	35	41	35	12
x 3	x 4	x 5	x 7	x 9

54	67	89	91	23
x 7	x 9	x 8	x 9	x 6

If there are three 5-a-side football teams on a coach, how many players are there altogether?

☐ x ☐ = ☐

If 5 coaches set off to watch the football match and each coach has 19 people on board, how many people are going to watch the match?

☐ x ☐ = ☐

At the football ground there are 4 stands. Each stand has 128 people in it. How many people are there in the stands altogether?

☐ x ☐ = ☐

Solve these sums and problems.

34	35	41	33	62
x 5	x 6	x 5	x 5	x 3

40	17	21	31	43
x 3	x 2	x 1	x 9	x 6

A rounders squad has 15 children in it. If there are 8 rounders squads in the championship, how many people are in the championship altogether?

[ ] x [ ] = [ ]

Each team supporters' coach holds 25 people. If there are 5 coaches, how many supporters are there altogether?

[ ] x [ ] = [ ]

Solve these sums and problems.

27	32	51	61	24
x 5	x 4	x 3	x 5	x 6

30	49	53	25	44
x 6	x 8	x 7	x 2	x 7

A netball team has 7 children in it. If there are 8 netball teams in a tournament, how many children are in the tournament altogether?

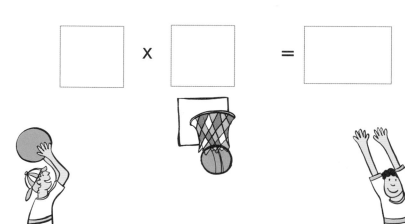

☐ x ☐ = ☐

The netball tournament has a break half-way through. If there should be 2 drinks for each child, how many drinks should there be altogether?

☐ x ☐ = ☐

Division sums are about **sharing** numbers equally.

Example: 4 ÷ 2 = ☐

It makes it easier to work this out if you draw some pictures.

Each child gets 2 cakes each. So, 4 shared between 2 is 2.

You can now fill in the answer to the sum: 4 ÷ 2 = 2

Example: 9 ÷ 3 = ☐

Each child gets 3 chocolate bars each. So, 9 shared between 3 is 3.

You can now fill in the answer to the sum: 9 ÷ 3 = 3

Share each group of objects below between three.

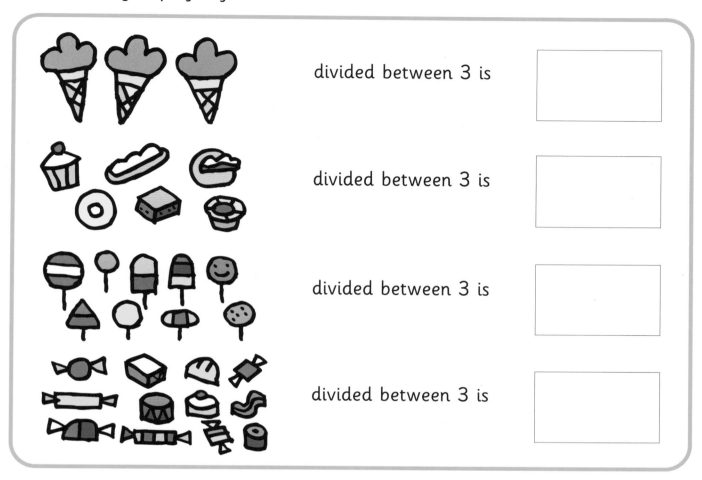

divided between 3 is

divided between 3 is

divided between 3 is

divided between 3 is

Fill in the missing numbers.

12 shared between 4 is

15 shared between 3 is

14 shared between 2 is

24 shared between 6 is

30 shared between 10 is

Division

Share each group of objects below between four.

divided between 4 is

divided between 4 is

divided between 4 is

divided between 4 is

Fill in the missing numbers.

15 shared between 5 is

10 shared between 2 is

16 shared between 4 is

9 shared between 3 is

18 shared between 2 is

Solve these division sums and problems.

10 ÷ 2 =	
12 ÷ 6 =	
6 ÷ 3 =	
18 ÷ 3 =	
20 ÷ 4 =	
25 ÷ 5 =	

12 ÷ 3 =	
16 ÷ 4 =	
30 ÷ 10 =	
28 ÷ 4 =	
50 ÷ 10 =	
20 ÷ 5 =	

If 20 pencils are shared equally between 10 children, how many does each child get?

Answer:

15 bottles of pop are shared between 5 shops. How many bottles does each shop get?

Answer:

How to do division sums

When division sums are set out like this, divide from the left.

Start with the tens and then divide the units.

Example:

T   U

3 fits into 6 twice, so write → **2   3** ← 3 fits into 9 three times, so
2 in the tens column   write 3 in the units column

3 | 6   9

Here is another example:

T   U

4 fits into 8 twice → **2   1** ← 4 fits into 4 once

4 | 8   4

Look at the sum below. It is slightly different.

T   U

3 fits into 6 twice → **2   2 r 1** ← 3 fits into 7 twice, **but**
                                      there is one left over!

3 | 6   7

We call the number that is left over a **remainder**, because it 'remains behind'.

The remainder is written after the answer with a little 'r'.

Solve these division sums and problems.

$$2\overline{)48} \qquad 5\overline{)55} \qquad 6\overline{)69}$$

$$9\overline{)99} \qquad 4\overline{)87} \qquad 3\overline{)38}$$

If there are 50 running shoes, how many pairs are there?

If 45 people travel to school on 5 buses, how many people are on each bus?

If £36 is shared equally between 3 people, how much does each person get?

page 7

18, 22, 22, 25, 19
eleven, eight, seventeen

page 8

28, 33, 28, 32, 25, 27, 31, 49

page 9

24, 30, 26, 32, 49, 48, 38, 31

page 11

14, 13, 11, 10
1, 11, 6, 5

page 12

6, 12, 9, 6, 9
six, five, five

page 13

40, 31, 11, 24
9, 32, 10, 24

page 15

10, 3, 5, 8, 9, 5
10 + 5, 20 − 5, 9 + 6

page 17

39, 47, 79, 77
57, 54, 89

page 19

57, 45, 112, 423
228, 359, 456

page 21

45, 3, 26, 50, 3
47p, 50p, 35p

page 23

59, 8, 39, 62, 7
123 − 78 = 45
123 − 78 = 45
112 − 79 = 33
200 − 112 = 88

page 25

45 + 12 = 57
90 + 50 = 140
70 − 40 = 30
25 + 12 = 37
70 − 30 = 40

page 26

11, 2, 10, 70, 16, 70

Team	Won	Drew	Lost	Points
United	4	1	3	21
City	5	2	1	25
Flint	3	4	1	21
Crewe	4	3	1	23
Mold	4	4	0	24

Winner: City

page 27

7, 10, 12, 20, 17, 20

	Mon	Tues	Wed	Thurs	Fri	Sat	Sun
Big Dipper	2	5	9	3	2	8	9
Log Flume	1	6	9	2	6	9	7
Rapids	8	11	3	9	6	2	7
Total visitors per day	11	22	21	14	14	19	23

On which day did the most people visit the theme park?   Sunday

page 29

2 x 4 = 8
4 x 3 = 12
3 x 3 = 9
4 x 4 = 16
3 x 4 = 12

page 31

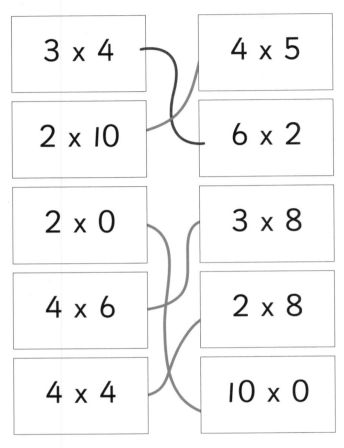

3 x 4	4 x 5
2 x 10	6 x 2
2 x 0	3 x 8
4 x 6	2 x 8
4 x 4	10 x 0

5	10	15	20	25	30	35	40	45	50
3	6	9	12	15	18	21	24	27	30
10	20	30	40	50	60	70	80	90	100

page 33

69, 140, 205, 245, 108
378, 603, 712, 819, 138
5 x 3 = 15
19 x 5 = 95
128 x 4 = 512

page 34

170, 210, 205, 165, 186
120, 34, 21, 279, 258
15 x 8 = 120
25 x 5 = 125

page 35

135, 128, 153, 305, 144
180, 392, 371, 50, 308
8 x 7 = 56
56 x 2 = 112

page 37

3 divided between 3 is 1,
6 divided between 3 is 2,
9 divided between 3 is 3,
12 divided between 3 is 4.

12 shared between 4 is 3,
15 shared between 3 is 5,
14 shared between 2 is 7,
24 shared between 6 is 4,
30 shared between 10 is 3.

page 38

4 divided between 4 is 1,
8 divided between 4 is 2,
12 divided between 4 is 3,
16 divided between 4 is 4.
15 shared between 5 is 3,
10 shared between 2 is 5,
16 shared between 4 is 4,
9 shared between 3 is 3,
18 shared between 2 is 9.

page 39

$10 \div 2 = 5$
$12 \div 6 = 2$
$6 \div 3 = 2$
$18 \div 3 = 6$
$20 \div 4 = 5$
$25 \div 5 = 5$

$12 \div 3 = 4$
$16 \div 4 = 4$
$30 \div 10 = 3$
$28 \div 4 = 7$
$50 \div 10 = 5$
$20 \div 5 = 4$

Each child gets 2 pencils.
Each shop gets 3 bottles of pop.

page 41

24, 11, 11r3, 11, 21r3, 12r2

There are 25 pairs of running shoes.
There are 9 people on each bus.
Each person gets £12.

How did you do?

+, add, addition, more, plus, make, sum, total, equals, count on, altogether, how many?

−, subtract, subtraction, take away, minus, difference between, more than, less than, fewer than, borrow, carry, carry-over.

x, multiply, multiplication, lots of, groups of, column, units, tens, hundreds.

÷, divide, division, share equally, remainder, left over, pattern.

After working through each section, put a tick in the box to show how you feel about the topic.

If you tick 'Not sure', go back to those pages and try again.

	Confident	Not sure
Adding with a number line		
Subtracting with a number line		
Addition sums		
Subtraction sums		
Addition and subtraction problems		
How to multiply		
Multiplication sums		
How to divide		
Division sums		

Even numbers end in:
0, 2, 4, 6 or 8.
Odd numbers end in:
1, 3, 5, 7 or 9.

Example: Ring the odd numbers.

12   (7)   (19)   (21)   16   30   (45)

The numbers that have rings around them are **odd** because they end in odd numbers.

Even and odd numbers make **patterns** when they are added together.

even number + even number = even number

even number + odd number = odd number

odd number + odd number = even number

If you add 6 + 2 (two even numbers) the answer will be even: 8.

If you add 8 + 3 (an even and odd number) the answer will be odd: 11.

If you add 5 + 3 (two odd numbers) the answer will be even: 8.

Colour the odd numbers green and the even numbers blue.

Four rabbits are having a race. Add together the number of the rabbit that came first with the number of the rabbit that came last.
Do you get an odd or even number?

Take away the number of the rabbit that came second from the number of the rabbit that came first. Do you get an odd or even number?

Number squares help you plan and predict number patterns.

1	2	3	4	5	6	7	8	9	10
11	12	13	14	15	16	17	18	19	20
21	22	23	24	25	26	27	28	29	30
31	32	33	34	35	36	37	38	39	40
41	42	43	44	45	46	47	48	49	50
51	52	53	54	55	56	57	58	59	60
61	62	63	64	65	66	67	68	69	70
71	72	73	74	75	76	77	78	79	80
81	82	83	84	85	86	87	88	89	90
91	92	93	94	95	96	97	98	99	100

In this number square, some of the numbers have been shaded.

These numbers have made a pattern of a straight line on one side of the square.

The shaded numbers all have something in common — they all end in 0, and are called **multiples** of 10.

They are multiples of 10 because they can be divided by 10 and are in the 10 times table.

So if a number ends in 0 you know it is a multiple of 10.

Lots more patterns can be found in a number square.

Just look at the multiples and see how many you can find!

Put a red dot in every third square.
Start with 3, and then 6, until you reach 99.

Put a green dot in every ninth square.
Start with 9, and then 18, until you reach 99.

What do you notice about where the red and green dots are?

1	2	3	4	5	6	7	8	9	10
11	12	13	14	15	16	17	18	19	20
21	22	23	24	25	26	27	28	29	30
31	32	33	34	35	36	37	38	39	40
41	42	43	44	45	46	47	48	49	50
51	52	53	54	55	56	57	58	59	60
61	62	63	64	65	66	67	68	69	70
71	72	73	74	75	76	77	78	79	80
81	82	83	84	85	86	87	88	89	90
91	92	93	94	95	96	97	98	99	100

Now put a blue dot in every fifth square.

Look at the numbers in the squares with both green and blue dots.
Write them out in the spaces below.

Number patterns help you to understand the relationship between numbers.

Here is an example: Look at the patterns below.
Work out the difference between the numbers in each line.
Then write in the missing numbers to finish each pattern.

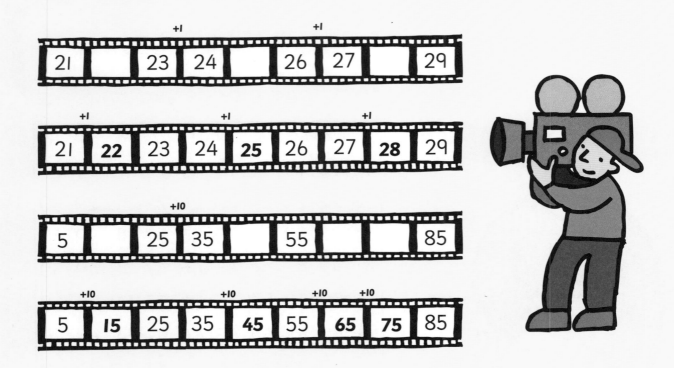

The frog is leaping in 4s, so the next leaf he lands on is 16.

Here are some number trails.
Look closely at each pattern. Fill in the missing numbers.

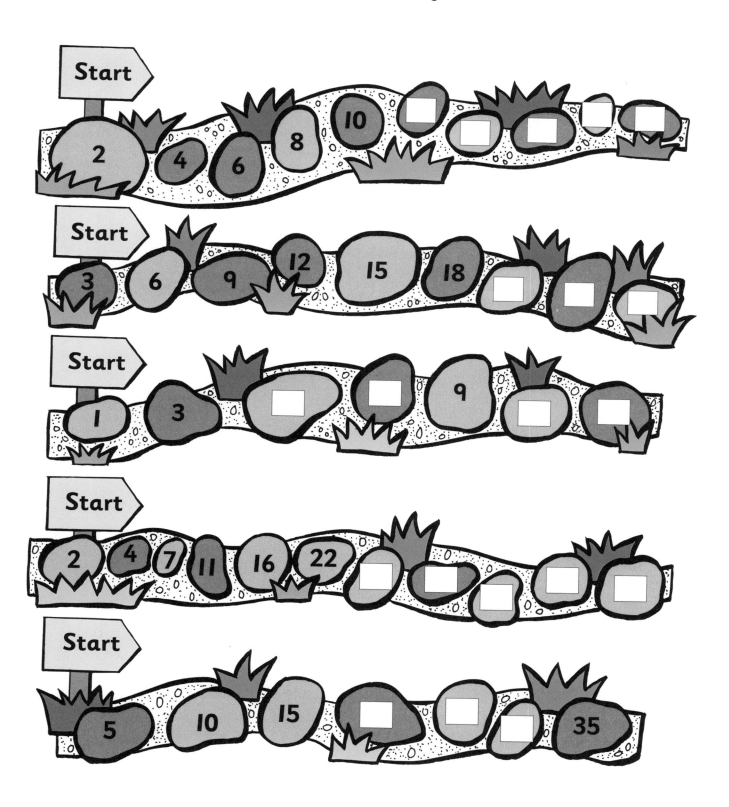

Numbers are made up of **units**, **tens** or **hundreds**.

A one-digit number is made up of units – 5

A two-digit number is made up of units and tens – 55

A three-digit number is made up of units, tens and hundreds – 555

H	T	U	
		6	6 units
	2	3	2 tens, 3 units
7	4	9	7 hundreds, 4 tens and 9 units

So, the **position** of a number tells you about its place value – whether it is units, tens or hundreds.

An **abacus** can help you to see the different parts of a number.

It can also help with sums. Add up all the counters in each column.

Example: 234 + 412 = ⬚

2 3 4   4 1 2   6 4 6

234 + 412 = 646

How many different numbers can Teddy make using these cards?

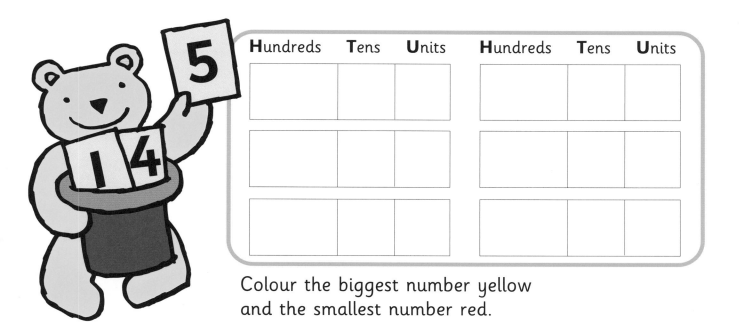

Hundreds	Tens	Units	Hundreds	Tens	Units

Colour the biggest number yellow
and the smallest number red.

Write down the number each abacus shows.

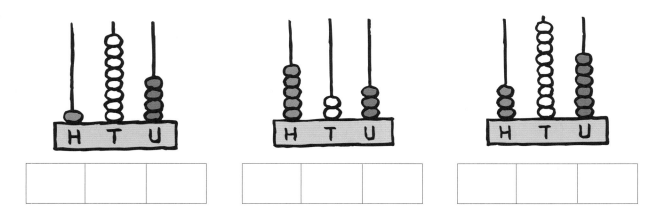

Now make each abacus show the number below it.

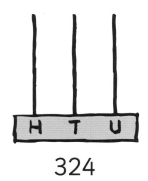

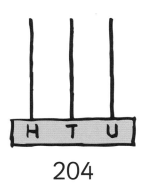

497   324   204

Write in the missing numbers.
Use the abacus to help you remember place value.

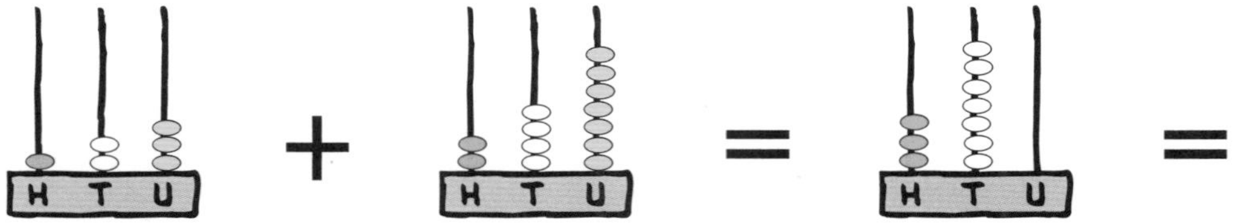

123 + 247 = = 370

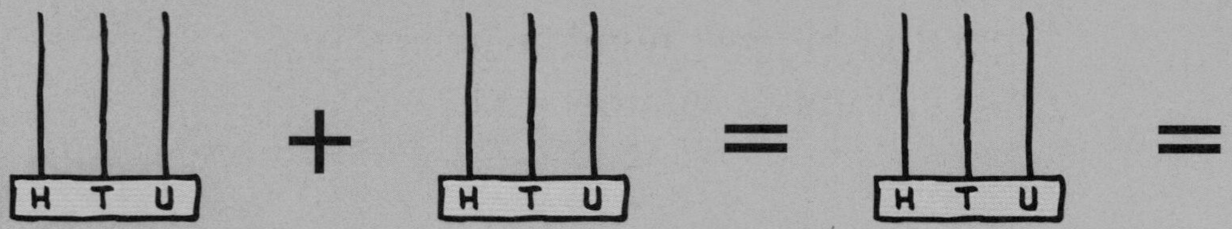

129 + 161 = =

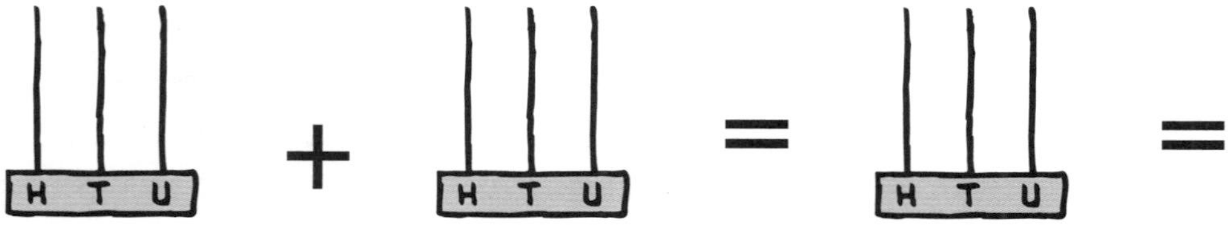

125 + 154 = =

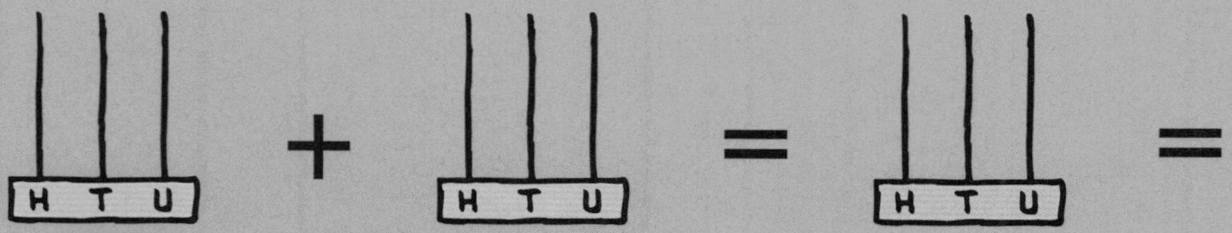

136 + 223 = =

Write in the missing numbers.
Use the abacus to help you remember place value.

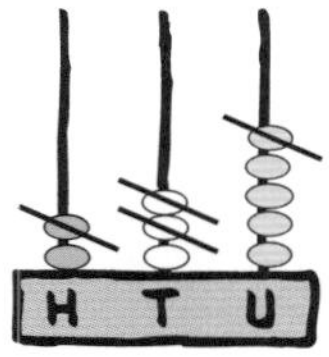

235 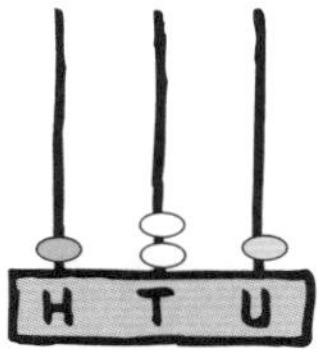 − 121 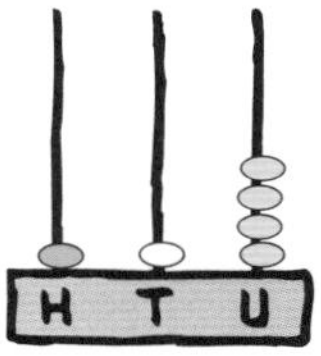 = = 114

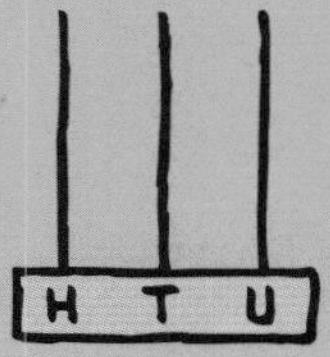

506 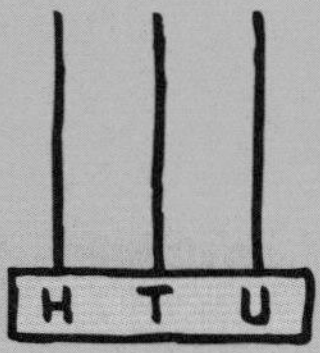 − 104 = =

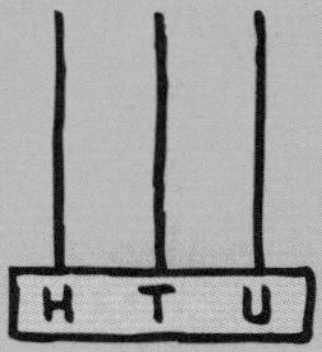

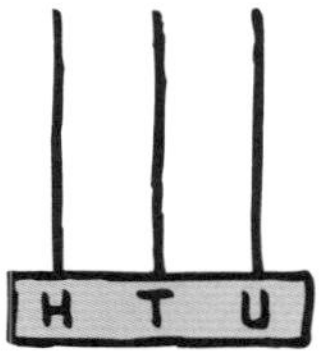

124 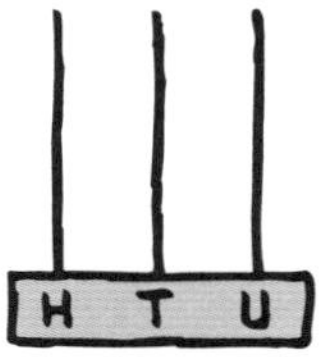 − 122 = =

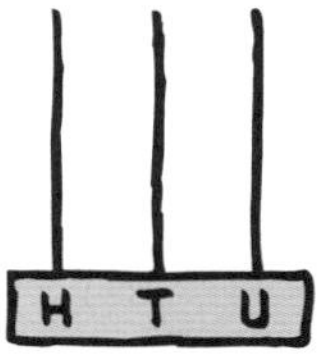

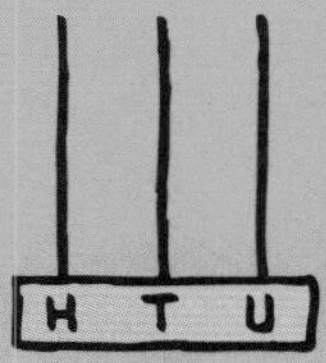

730 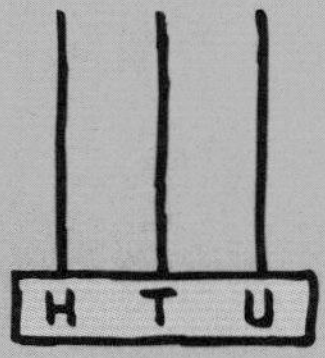 − 120 = =

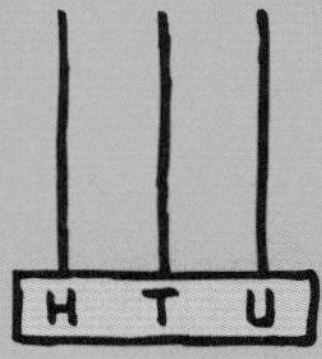

A fraction is a **part** of something.

A fraction can be part of a number or part of a shape.

Example:

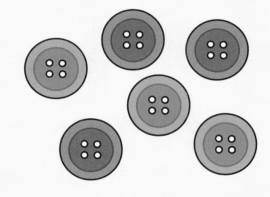

A fraction of this cake
has been cut.

A fraction of these buttons
are shaded.

A 'half' is a fraction of something that is split into **two** equal parts.

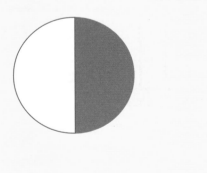

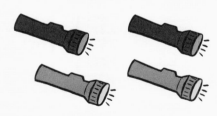

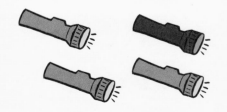

A 'quarter' is a fraction of something that is split into **four** equal parts.

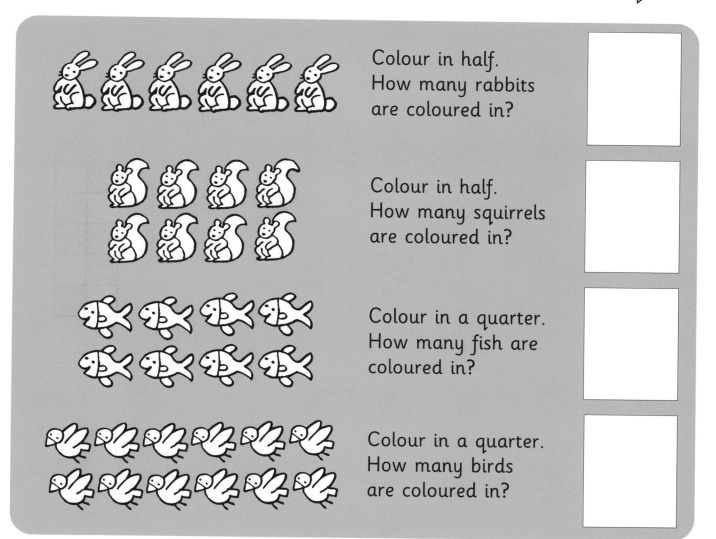

Colour in half.
How many rabbits
are coloured in?

Colour in half.
How many squirrels
are coloured in?

Colour in a quarter.
How many fish are
coloured in?

Colour in a quarter.
How many birds
are coloured in?

Colour in half of each shape.

Colour in a quarter of each shape.

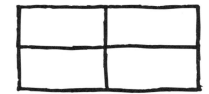
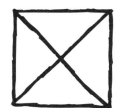

Fractions are written using two sets of numbers.

 → The top number tells you the number of parts you are looking at.

→ The bottom number tells you how many parts the number or shape is split into.

$\frac{1}{2}$ is one out of two parts

$\frac{3}{4}$ is three out of four parts

$\frac{6}{10}$ is six out of ten parts

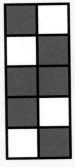

So a **half** written as a fraction is $\frac{1}{2}$.

A **quarter** written as a fraction is $\frac{1}{4}$.

A **third** written as a fraction is $\frac{1}{3}$.

Here are some other names to learn:

$\frac{1}{5}$ = fifth $\frac{1}{6}$ = sixth $\frac{1}{7}$ = seventh $\frac{1}{8}$ = eighth

What do you notice about this pattern?

In most cases we talk about fractions by adding **th** to the bottom number.

Let's look at these:

$\frac{3}{8}$ = three-eighths $\frac{4}{10}$ = four-tenths $\frac{3}{4}$ = three-quarters

Write the number of coloured balls as a fraction of the total number.

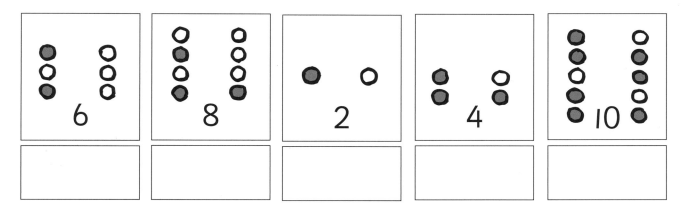

What fraction is coloured? Write the word underneath.

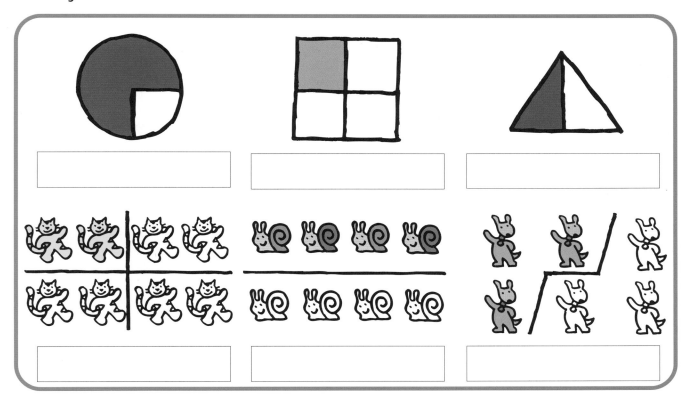

Colour in the correct amount.

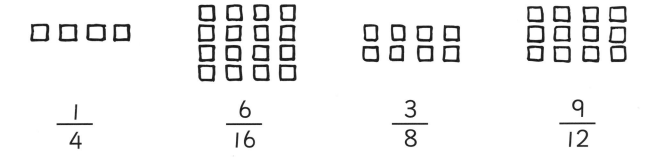

$$\frac{1}{4}$$ $$\frac{6}{16}$$ $$\frac{3}{8}$$ $$\frac{9}{12}$$

Colour in the fraction given of each of these shapes.

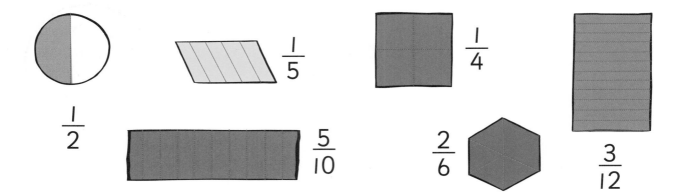

$\frac{1}{2}$

$\frac{1}{5}$

$\frac{5}{10}$

$\frac{1}{4}$

$\frac{2}{6}$

$\frac{3}{12}$

If I eat half of these ice creams, how many are left?

Colour in half of a hundred and a quarter of 160.

The zookeeper is very busy.

He has to feed $\frac{3}{4}$ of the monkeys.
How many is this?

He has to wash $\frac{1}{3}$ of the elephants.
How many is this?

He has to feed $\frac{1}{4}$ of the penguins.
How many is this?

He has to exercise $\frac{1}{2}$ of the birds.
How many is this?

How many animals in total has the zookeeper looked after today?

page 49

green: 1, 3, 5, 7, 9, 11, 13, 15
blue: 2, 4, 6, 8, 10, 12, 14

4 + 3 = 7 **odd**
4 − 1 = 3 **odd**

page 51

Any reasonable explanation
of patterns.
45, 90

page 52

22, 25, 28
15, 45, 65, 75

page 53

2, 4, 6, 8, 10, 12, 14, 16, 18, 20
3, 6, 9, 12, 15, 18, 21, 24, 27
1, 3, 5, 7, 9, 11, 13
2, 4, 7, 11, 16, 22, 29, 37, 46, 56, 67
5, 10, 15, 20, 25, 30, 35

page 55

145, 154, 415, 451, 514, 541
Yellow: 541, Red: 145
184, 523, 396

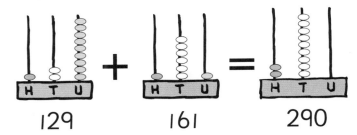

page 56

129   161   290

125   154   279

136   223   359

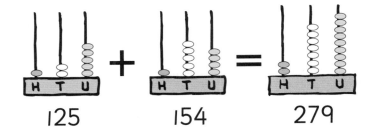

page 57

506   104   402

124   122   2

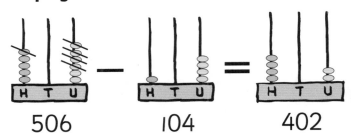
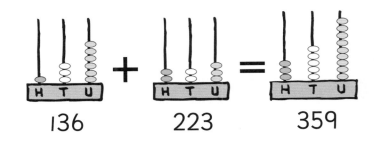

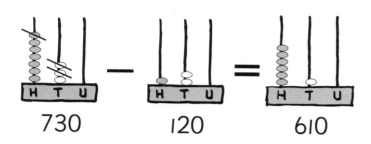

730   120   610

page 59

3, 4, 2, 3

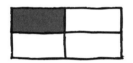

page 61

$\frac{2}{6}$ $\frac{3}{8}$ $\frac{1}{2}$ $\frac{3}{4}$ $\frac{7}{10}$

three-quarters, a quarter, half,
two- eighths, four-eighths, three-sixths

page 62

$\frac{1}{2}$

$\frac{1}{5}$ $\frac{1}{4}$

$\frac{5}{10}$

$\frac{2}{6}$ $\frac{3}{12}$

2 ice creams

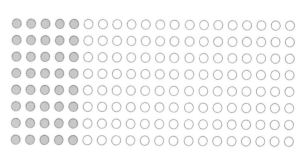

page 63

3, 1, 2, 10, 16

odd, even

first, second, third ..., last

pattern

multiple of

place value

units, tens, hundreds

abacus

fraction

part, equal parts

half, quarter, third, fifth, sixth, tenth, twelfth

After working through each section, put a tick in the box to show how you feel about the topic.

If you tick 'Not sure' go back to those pages and try again.

	Confident	Not sure
Odd and even numbers	⬭	⬭
Number patterns	⬭	⬭
Place value	⬭	⬭
Fractions	⬭	⬭

Very well done!

When you are adding up lots of different coins, it makes it easier if you start with the largest amount first.

Rearrange the coins starting with the largest amount.

50p + 2p + 2p + 1p = 55p

Remember, there are 100 pence in £1.

So, in £2 there are 200p and in £1.40 there are 140p.

When you add up pounds and pence together use a **decimal point** to separate the pounds from the pence.

Make sure you write out the amounts neatly in columns, and keep the **decimal point** in the same place.

Example: 55p + £1.05 =   £1.60

Lay the sum out like an ordinary addition sum, but remember to keep the decimal point in the same place, with pounds on the left and pence on the right.

```
  £ 1 . 0 5
+ £ 0 . 5 5
  £ 1 . 6 0
    ↑     ↑
 pounds  pence
```

Match the total of coins in each box with the amounts at the side. Draw a line between each pair.

(5p) (1p) (1p)	**24p**
(20p) (10p) (5p)	**£1.15**
(50p) (5p) (5p)	**35p**
(2p) (2p) (10p) (10p)	**7p**
(5p)	**60p**

How much money would you need to buy these things?

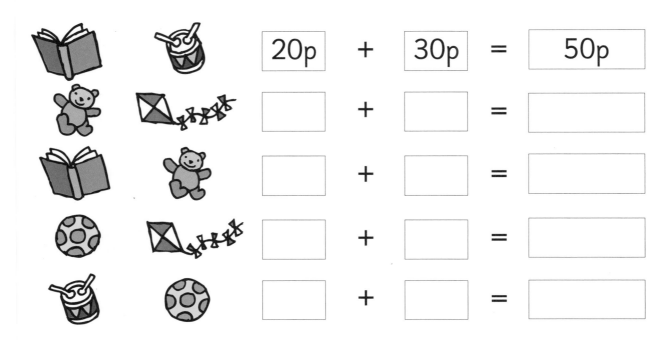

		20p	+	30p	=	50p
			+		=	
			+		=	
			+		=	
			+		=	

Draw a line to match the price of each item with the amount of money in each purse.

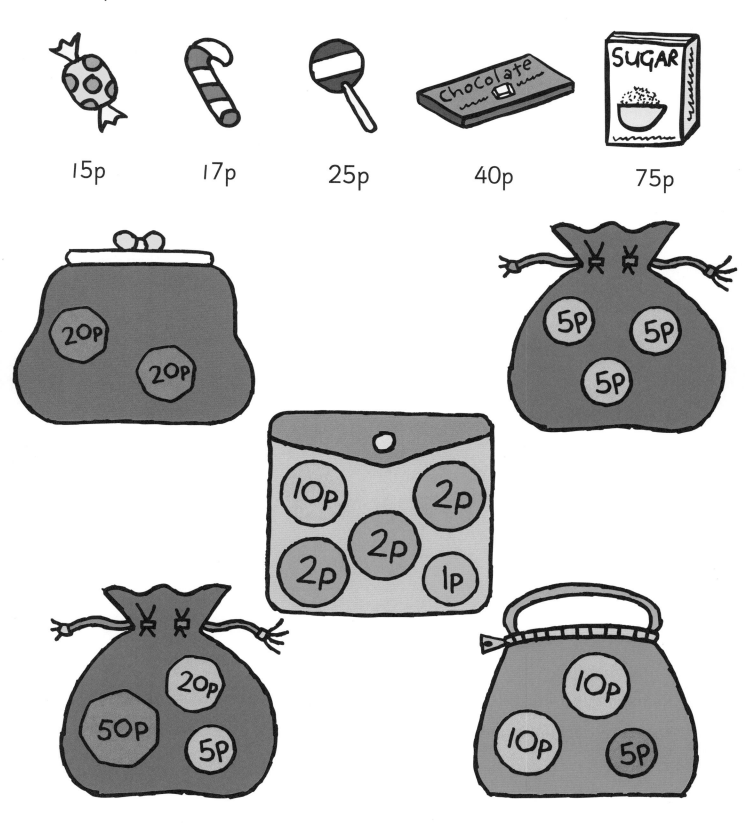

15p   17p   25p   40p   75p

10p can be made up of lots of different sets of coins.

(5p) + (5p) = (10p)

(5p) + (2p) + (2p) + (1p) = (10p)

(5p) + (2p) + (1p) + (1p) + (1p) = (10p)

Just remember that it's easier to add up money starting with the largest amount first.

When you have to work out change all you need to do is a subtraction sum.

Example: How much change would you get from £1 if you bought a notebook for 65p?

$$\pounds \; {}^0\cancel{1} \; . \; {}^9\cancel{0} \; {}^1\cancel{0}$$
$$- \pounds \; 0 \; . \; 6 \; 5$$
$$\boxed{\pounds \; 0 \; . \; 3 \; 5}$$

Remember to lay this out as an ordinary subtraction sum and to keep the decimal point in the same place.

All four children had £1 pocket money.
This is how much they each have left.
Work out how much each of them spent.

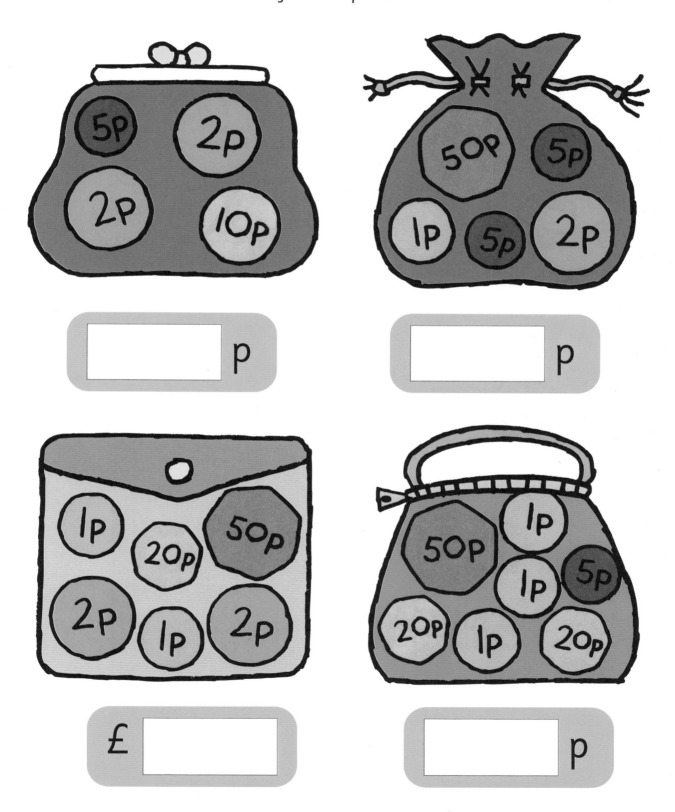

p

p

£

p

Colour in the coins to make the right amounts.

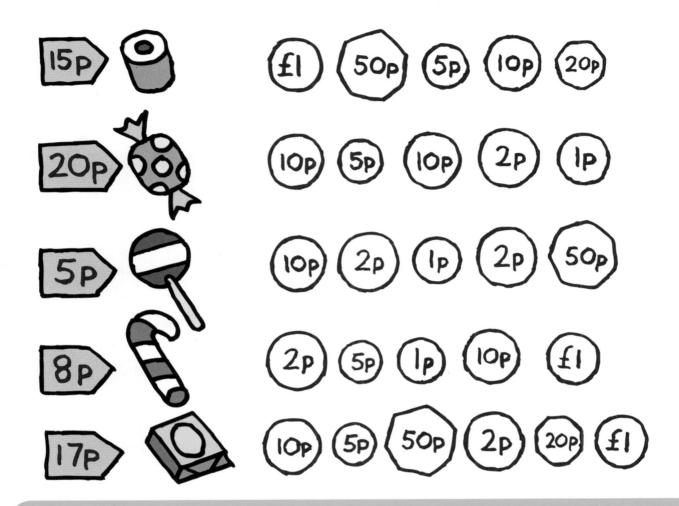

15p

20p

5p

8p

17p

£1 50p 5p 10p 20p

10p 5p 10p 2p 1p

10p 2p 1p 2p 50p

2p 5p 1p 10p £1

10p 5p 50p 2p 20p £1

How much change do you get from £1.00?

50p — toy costing 50p

60p — toy costing 60p

10p — toy costing 10p

Fill in the blank coins to make the correct amounts.

◯ + ◯ = **2p**

◯ + ◯ + ◯ + ◯ = **5p**

◯ + ◯ = **10p**

◯ + ◯ + ◯ = **20p**

◯ + ◯ + ◯ = **50p**

Write down as many ways as you can find to make £1.

How much money does each child have?

  Hassan _____

  Rachel _____

   Razia _____

   Nigel _____

 Jonathan _____

   Harriet _____

Who has the most money?

How much more money has Jonathan than Hassan?

What is the difference between Harriet's money and Rachel's money?

The children put all their money together. How much money is there altogether?

 Hassan   Rachel   Razia   Nigel   Jonathan   Harriet

Look at this shop window.

baking tray £1.38

flour 99p

cream £1.53

Cornflakes £1.55

chocolate 34p

sugar 78p

Now look at these shopping lists. Each child has £5. How much will each child spend, and how much change will they get?

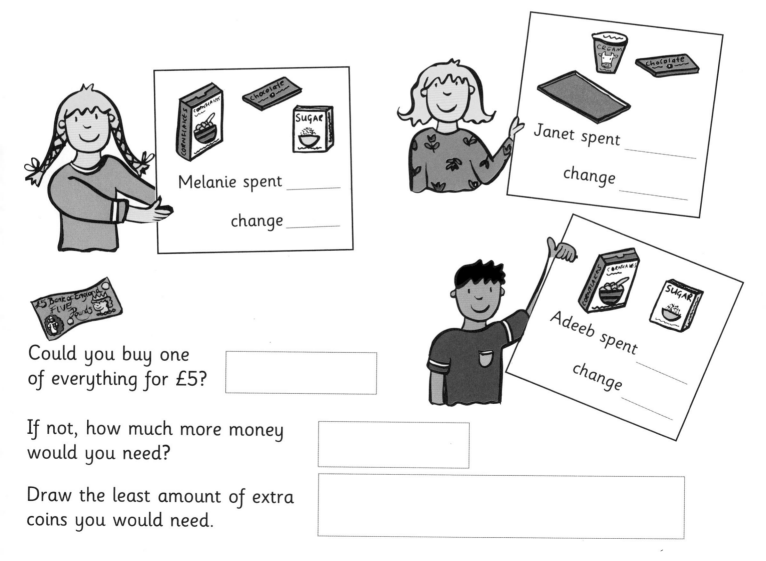

Melanie spent _____

change _____

Janet spent _____

change _____

Adeeb spent _____

change _____

Could you buy one of everything for £5?

If not, how much more money would you need?

Draw the least amount of extra coins you would need.

page 69

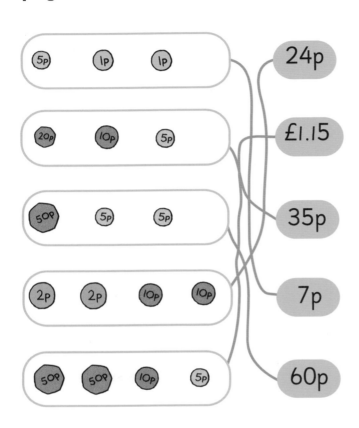

24p

£1.15

35p

7p

60p

page 70

£1.00 + £1.50 = £2.50
20p + £1.00 = £1.20
50p + £1.50 = £2.00
30p + 50p = 80p

page 71

15p

17p

25p

40p

75p

page 73

81p, 37p, 24p, 2p

page 74

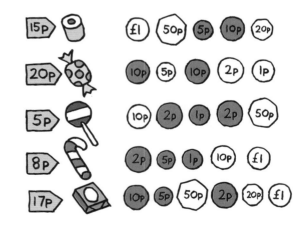

50p, 40p, 90p

page 75

$$1p + 1p = 2p$$
$$2p + 1p + 1p + 1p = 5p$$
$$5p + 5p = 10p$$
$$10p + 5p + 5p = 20p$$
$$20p + 20p + 10p = 50p$$

Parent to check coins that equal £1.

page 76

Hassan – 90p
Rachel – £1.10
Razia – £1.11
Nigel – £2.00
Jonathan – £1.15
Harriet – £2.75

Harriet has the most money.
Jonathan has got 25p more
than Hassan.
There is a difference of £1.65 between
Harriet's money and Rachel's money.
There is £9.01 altogether.

page 77

Melanie spent £2.67
change £2.33

Janet spent £3.25
change £1.75

Adeeb spent £2.33
change £2.67

No, you could not buy one of
everything for £5.
You would need £1.57 more.

money

coin

amount

penny, pence, pound (£)

decimal point

how much?

change

buy, bought

cost

spend

After working through each section, put a tick in the box to show how you feel about the topic.

If you tick 'Not sure' go back to those pages and try again.

	Confident	Not sure
Adding money		
Money equations		

Look at this table.

The table is split into two **columns**: one for 'names' and one for the number of times a group of children can jump in 10 seconds.

Name	Jumps
Claire	7
Harry	8
Jack	13
Sophie	9
Stella	7

You can use the information in the table to answer these questions:

Who can do the most jumps?

Jack

Who can do one more jump than Harry?

Sophie

How many more jumps can Sophie do than Claire?

2

Which two children did the same number of jumps?

Claire and Stella

A class of 20 children had a vote to say what their favourite snack is. The results are shown in this table.

Favourite snack	Votes
Chocolate	3
Crisps	10
Fruit	6
Ice-cream	1

Which snack had 3 votes?

Which snack is the most popular?

Which snack is the least popular?

How many more votes did crisps have than chocolate?

How many more votes did fruit have than ice-cream?

A pictogram is a special way of showing information by using pictures.

Look at this pictogram. It shows the colour of hair of the children in Class 2.

Each child is shown by a smiley face ☺.

Red | ☺☺

Blond | ☺☺☺☺☺☺

Brown | ☺☺☺☺☺☺

Children in Class 2

To find out how many children have a certain hair colour, you can count the number of faces next to that colour.

How many children have blond hair?   7

How many children have brown hair?   6

How many children have red hair?   2

How many children are in Class 2 altogether?   15

This pictogram shows the colour of eyes of children in Class 3.
This time **two** children are shown by one smiley face.

Brown ☺☺☺☺☺☺

Hazel ☺

Blue ☺☺☺☺

Green ☺☺☺

Children in Class 3

How many children have brown eyes?

How many children have green eyes?

Do most children have blue or brown eyes?

How many less children have hazel
eyes than blue eyes?

How many children are there in Class 3
altogether?

Bar charts are a good way of sorting information about a topic.

This bar chart
shows 20 children's
favourite fruit.

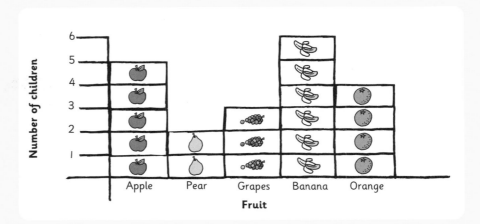

The different fruits are labelled along the bottom, and the number of children that prefer each fruit are labelled up the side.

You can use the information on the bar chart to answer these questions.

How many children prefer apples?

5

How many more children prefer
bananas than oranges?

2

Which fruit is the most popular in the class?

Bananas

Look at the chart below. It shows how the children in one class get to school.

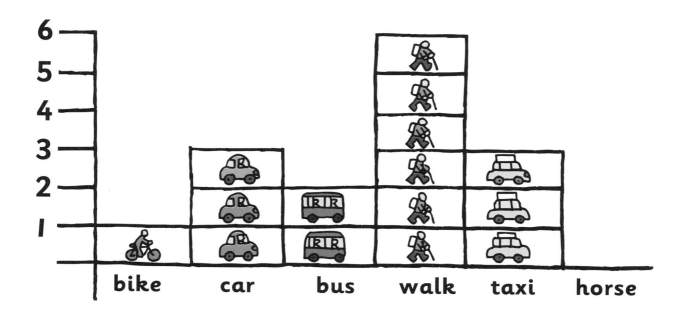

How many children come to school by bus?

How many children walk to school?

How many children come by car or taxi?

How many more children walk to school than come on their bikes?

Two children come to school on a horse! Show this on the chart.

Look at the chart below.

It shows how many children in one class have school dinners, packed lunches or go home.

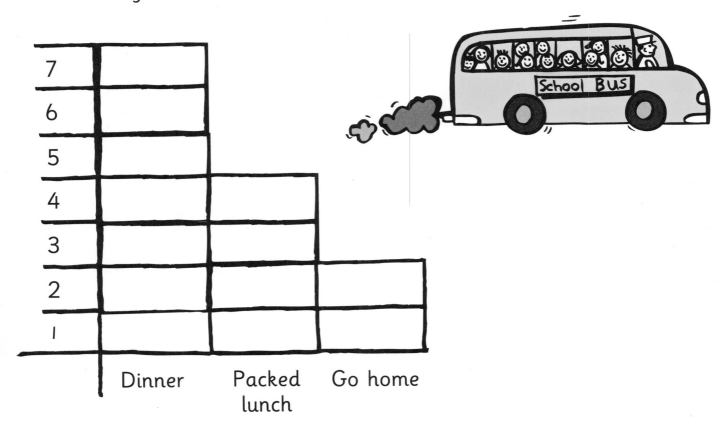

How many children have school dinners?

How many children have packed lunches?

How many more children have school dinners than packed lunches?

How many less children go home than have packed lunches?

Look at this bar chart. The shaded areas show how many days off the teachers had in a year.

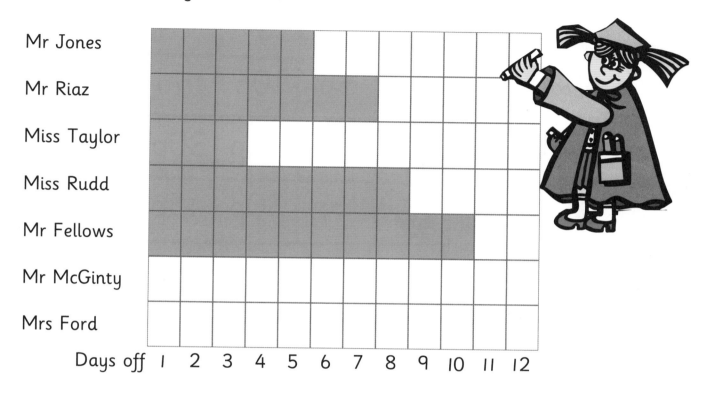

How many days off did each teacher have?

Mr Jones	Mr Riaz	Miss Taylor	Miss Rudd	Mr Fellows

Who had the most time off?

Fill in the chart with the following information:

Mr Fellows had two more days off.

Miss Taylor had just one more day off.

Two new teachers, Mr McGinty and Mrs Ford, came to the school.

Mr McGinty had seven days off and Mrs Ford had two days off less than Mr Fellows.

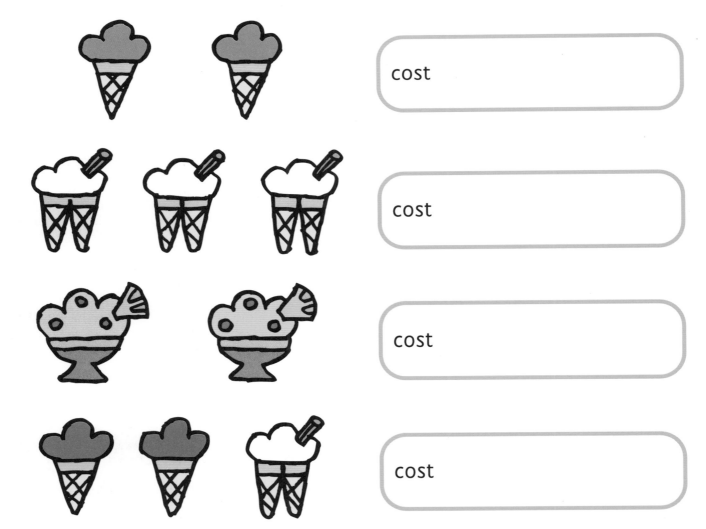

ICE-CREAM SHOP

Price list	one	two	three
🍦	5p	10p	15p
🍦	10p	20p	30p
🍨	15p	30p	45p

Use the chart to work out how much these ice creams will cost.

cost

cost

cost

cost

Here is a chart showing how much it costs to park in a car park.

Car Park Charges

Type of vehicle	1 hour	3 hours	8 hours
	60p	£1.80	£4.80
	£1	£3	£8
	£1.50	£4.50	£12

Use the chart to work out how much it will cost for these vehicles to park in the car park.

 3 hours   cost

 1 hour   cost

 8 hours   cost

1 hour   cost

 3 hours   cost

page 83

Chocolate had 3 votes.
Crisps is the most popular snack.
Ice cream is the least popular snack.
Crisps had 7 more votes
than chocolate.
Fruit had 5 more votes
than ice-cream.

page 85

12 children have brown eyes.
6 children have green eyes.
Most children have brown eyes.
6 less children have hazel eyes than
blue eyes.
There are 28 children in Class 3.

page 87

2 children come to school by bus.
6 children walk to school.
6 children come by car or taxi.
5 more children walk to school
than go on their bikes.

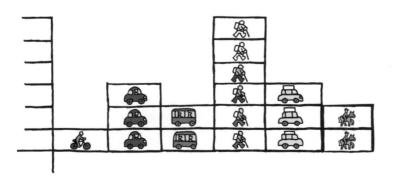

page 88

7 children have school dinners.
4 children have packed lunches.
3 more children have school
dinners than packed lunches.
2 less children go home than
have packed lunches.

page 89

Mr Jones – 5
Mr Riaz – 7
Miss Taylor – 3
Miss Rudd – 8
Mr Fellows – 10
Mr Fellows had the most time off.

	1	2	3	4	5	6	7	8	9	10	11	12
Mr Jones												
Mr Riaz												
Miss Taylor												
Miss Rudd												
Mr Fellows												
Mr McGinty												
Mrs Ford												

Days off 1 2 3 4 5 6 7 8 9 10 11 12

page 91

£1.80
£1
£12
60p
£3

page 90

10p
30p
30p
20p

Excellent work!

table

column

vote

pictogram

bar chart, chart

sort, count

label

most popular

After working through each section, put a tick in the box to show how you feel about the topic.

If you tick 'Not sure' go back to those pages and try again.

	Confident	Not sure
Reading tables		
Pictograms		
Bar charts		
Reading charts		

Two-dimensional shapes are **flat** shapes.

Flat shapes have different numbers of **sides** and **corners**, and/or different **lengths** of sides.

These are called a shape's **properties**.

You can match the name of a shape to its properties.

This shape is round	circle	●
This shape has 4 sides of equal length	square	■
This shape has 3 corners	triangle	▲
This shape has 5 corners and 5 sides	pentagon	⬠
This shape has 4 corners, 2 short sides and 2 long sides	rectangle	▬

Join the dots to make 6 different shapes.
Then draw a line from each shape to its name below.

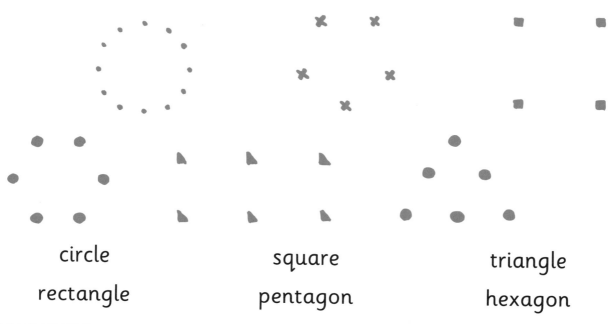

circle

square

triangle

rectangle

pentagon

hexagon

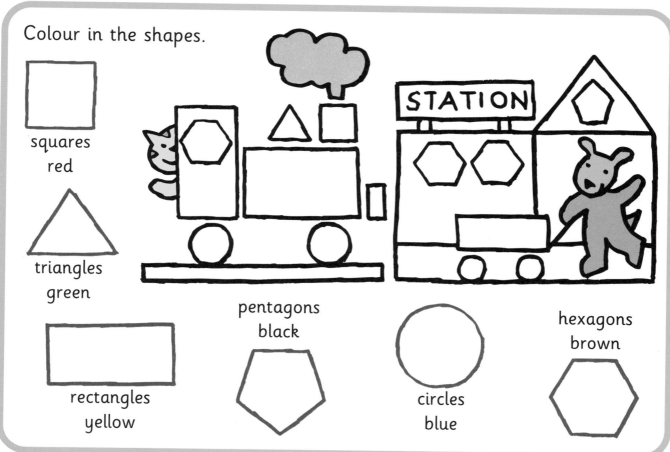

Colour in the shapes.

squares
red

triangles
green

rectangles
yellow

pentagons
black

circles
blue

hexagons
brown

Unscramble the words to find the names of these shapes.
Draw a line from the unscrambled words to the correct shapes.
The first one has been done for you.

qaseru   aetlnregc   iccerl   oehgaxn

square

ierlgnta   aegpotnn   ooatgcn   ikte

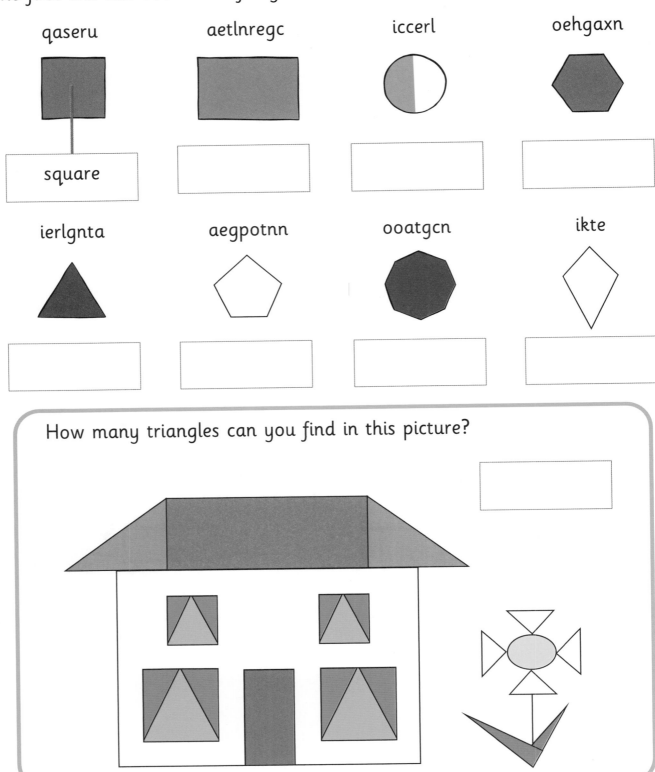

How many triangles can you find in this picture?

Write the correct names of the two-dimensional shapes in the boxes and then draw them.

I am round.

I have no corners and no edges.

I am a [   ]

I have straight sides.

I have 3 corners.

I am a [   ]

I have 4 straight sides that are different lengths.

I am a [   ]

I have 6 straight sides and 6 corners.

I am a [   ]

Three-dimensional shapes are **solid** or **hollow** shapes.

Three-dimensional shapes look lifelike and real. You can see 3D shapes all around you.

A box can be a **cube** or a **cuboid**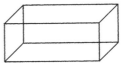

It is hollow because there is a space in its middle.

An empty baked-bean tin is a **cylinder** and is hollow.

Just like two-dimensional shapes, each shape has different properties.
These properties are number and length of sides, corners and surfaces.
3-D shapes can have **flat** or **curved** surfaces.

sphere　　　　**cone**　　　　**cylinder**

curved　　　　flat　curved　　　flat　curved

All these 3D shapes have curved surfaces.

The cone and the cylinder also have flat surfaces.

What are the names of these shapes?
Fill in the missing letters to find out.

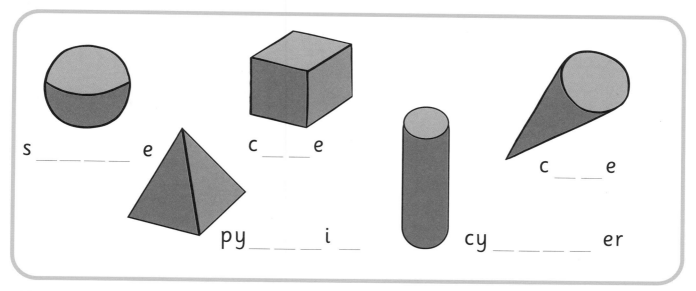

s _ _ _ _ _ _ e

c _ _ _ e

c _ _ e

py _ _ _ _ i _

cy _ _ _ _ _ _ er

Here is a clown. He is made up of lots of different shapes. Name each of the shapes that the clown is made from and draw a line to them.

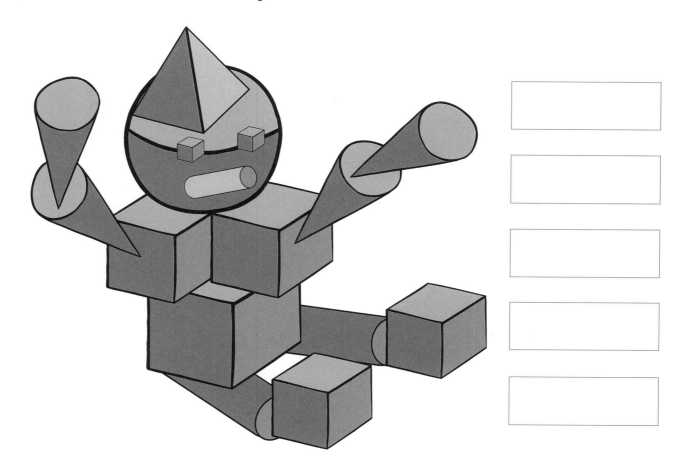

3D shapes

Colour in the shapes.

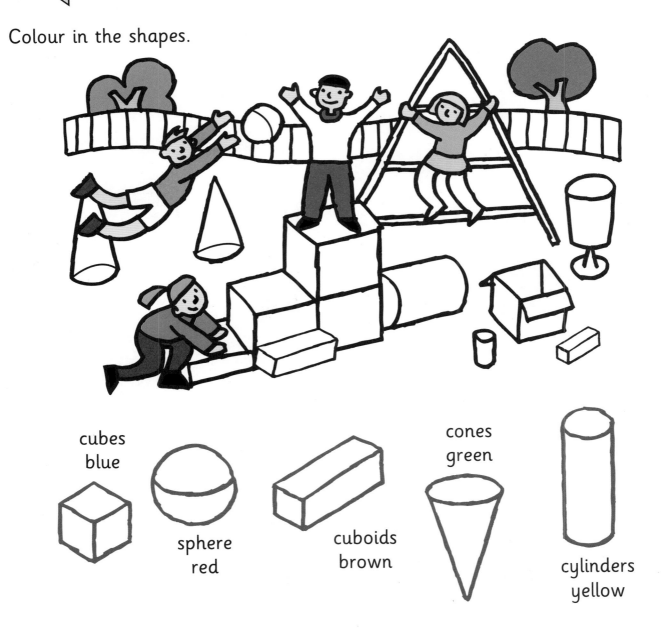

cubes
blue

sphere
red

cuboids
brown

cones
green

cylinders
yellow

Draw the shapes in the boxes below.

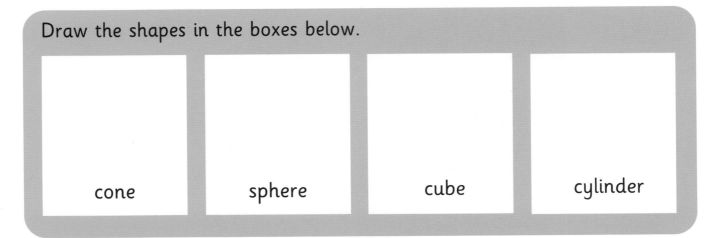

cone	sphere	cube	cylinder

Write the correct names of the three-dimensional shapes in the boxes and then draw them.

I have 6 faces.

I have 12 edges which are straight and of equal length.

I am a [ ]

I have 1 curved surface and no corners.

I am a [ ]

I have 8 corners.

I have 4 rectangular faces and 2 square faces.

I am a [ ]

I have 1 square face and 4 triangular faces.

I have 5 corners.

I am a [ ]

Symmetry can be found in shapes, objects and pictures.

A line of symmetry is an imaginary dividing line, which splits a shape into identical equal parts.

This book has 1 line of symmetry.   This lolly has 1 line of symmetry.

Symmetry is a bit like a reflection. If you place a mirror along the dotted line on the book, you will be able to see the identical reflection of half of the book.

Some shapes have more than one line of symmetry.

This flag has two lines of symmetry.

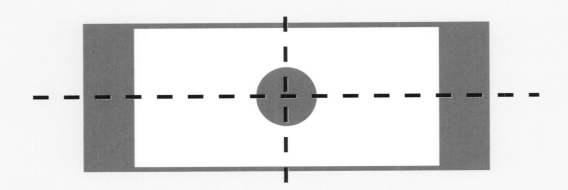

Draw the other side of these shapes at the dotted line.

Draw the line of symmetry on these pictures.

Draw the other parts of these shapes.
The dotted lines show where the lines
of symmetry are.

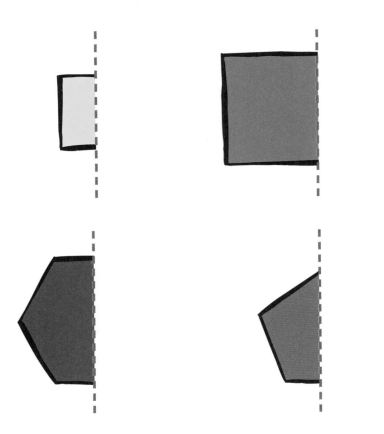

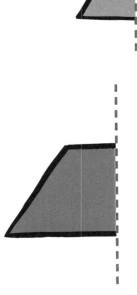

Draw in the lines of symmetry on these pictures.
There may be more than one.

Draw the other parts of these shapes.
The dotted lines show where some of the lines of
symmetry are. The first one has been done for you.

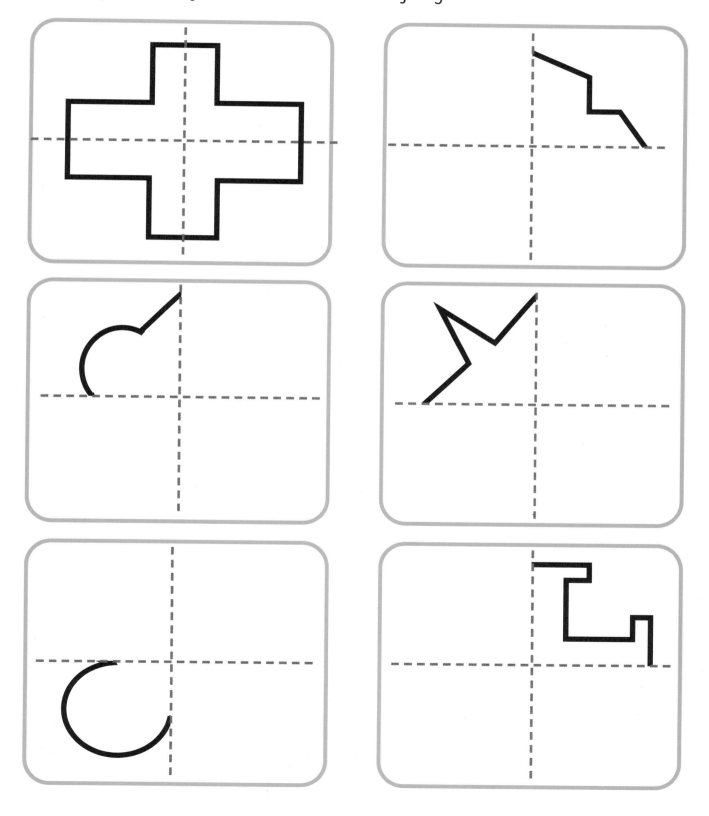

Length is usually measured in centimetres (cm) or metres (m).

Weight is usually measured in grams (g) or kilograms (kg).

Liquid is usually measured in pints or litres (l).

Before measuring something, it is sometimes helpful to estimate first. Estimate means to make a guess at how long or heavy something might be.

It helps to learn some common measurements first and then decide if your object is more or less than it.

A ruler is 30cm long   Milk comes in a pint

Example:

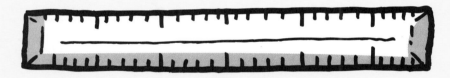

Estimation – 10cm   Real length – 11cm

Here are some words you can use to compare measurements:

longer, longest   shorter, shortest   taller, tallest

heavier, heaviest   lighter, lightest

Colour the biggest rocket yellow. How high is it?

Colour the smallest rocket green. How high is it?

Colour the other rocket blue.
Draw a rocket that is bigger than the yellow rocket.

Draw a line from each snake to the length you **estimate** it to be.

10cm

20cm

13cm

5cm

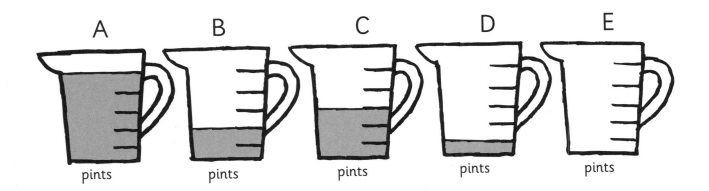

A   B   C   D   E

pints   pints   pints   pints   pints

Colour the jug that holds most in blue.
Colour the jug that holds least in green.
Colour the jug that holds 3 pints in yellow.
Colour jug E so that it holds TWICE as much as jug D.

Which is heavier, the car or
the dog?

How much does the parcel
weigh?

How would you measure these things?
Match the word and the object.

litres   grams   centimetres

Here is a parcel counter at the Post Office.
How much does each parcel on the scales weigh?

What would you use to measure these things?
Draw lines to match up the objects and the words.

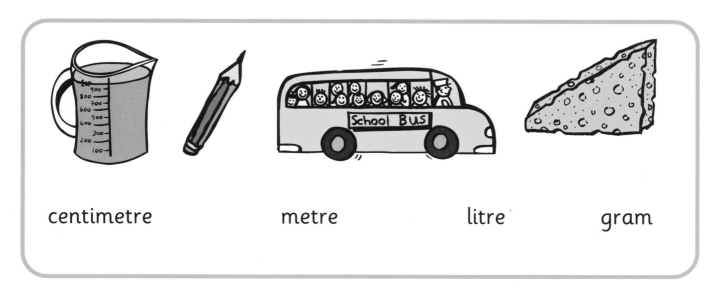

centimetre   metre   litre   gram

Measuring

Measure these lines with a ruler.

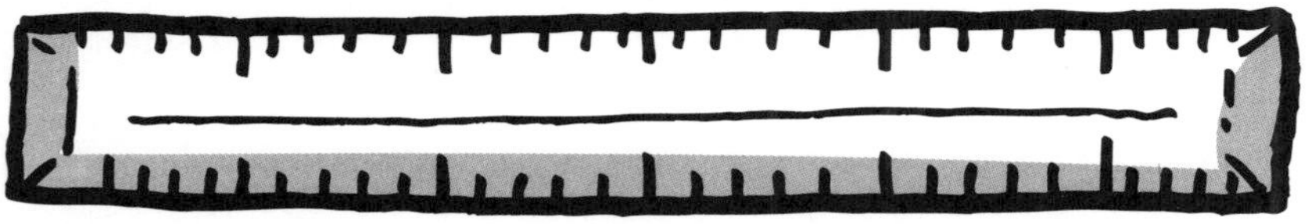

A ──────────────

B /\/\/\/\/\/\/\/\

C ──

D \/\/\/

How long is the longest line?

How long is the shortest line?

What is the difference in length between the longest and shortest lines?

Use a piece of string to cover the lines and then measure the string on a ruler to see how long the lines are.

A

B

C

D

How long is the longest line?

How long is the shortest line?

What is the difference in length between the longest and shortest lines?

There are 24 **hours** in each day.

There are 60 **minutes** in each hour.

There are 60 **seconds** in each minute.

The hours on a clock are shown by two clock-hands.
The short hand points to what hour it is, and the long hand points to how many minutes past the hour it is.

Example:

 The time is 2 o'clock

 The time is half-past 3

Digital clocks and watches show the time in a different way.

Example:

The time is 2 o'clock

The time is half-past 3

This shows hours, like the short hand

This shows how many minutes past, like the long hand

Write down the missing times for each clock.

4 o'clock

4:00

7:30

3:00

Party starts

Party finishes

How many hours did the party last?

	hours

Each number on a clock shows a 5-minute gap.

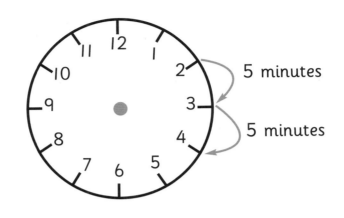

5 o'clock

5 minutes past 5

On a digital clock the same time would look like this:

Take a good look at this clock.

The time is 50 minutes past 3 or 3.50.

You can also say it is 10 minutes **to** 4 because there are 10 minutes left before it is 4 o'clock.

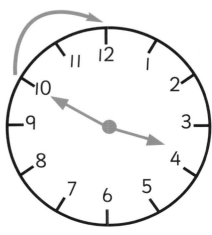

Write down the missing times for each clock.

10 minutes past 4		10 minutes past 1
4:10	3:50	

Write down the missing times for each clock.

		20 m
4:20		

The bus takes half an hour
Show the time it arrives o

What time does each of these clocks say?
Write the digital times below.

| : | : | : | : |

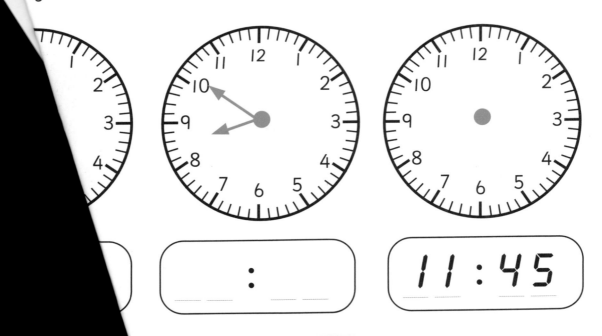

hese clocks.
digital time or draw in the hands on the clock face.

| : | 11:45 |

The giant has to get back to the beanstalk!
Fill in the right times on all the clocks along his journey and write the time he arrived back at the beanstalk.
Use a real clock to help you fill in this page.

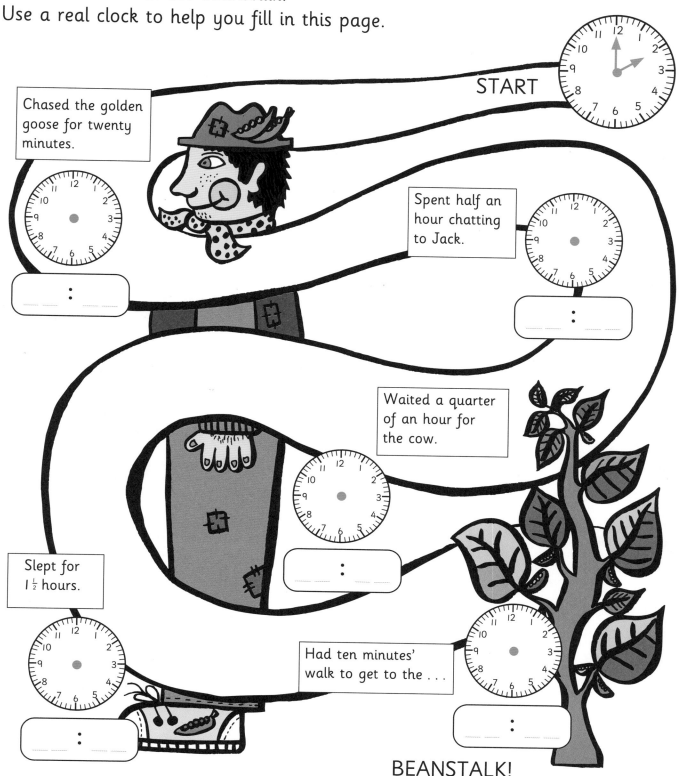

START

Chased the golden goose for twenty minutes.

Spent half an hour chatting to Jack.

Waited a quarter of an hour for the cow.

Slept for 1½ hours.

Had ten minutes' walk to get to the . . .

BEANSTALK!

page 97

circle

pentagon

square

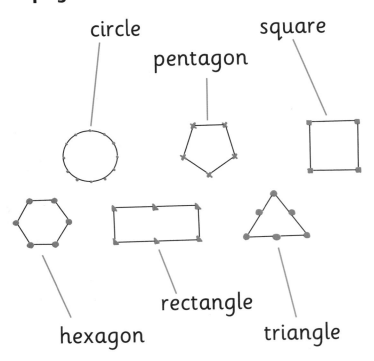

hexagon   triangle

rectangle

Parent to check colours of shapes.

page 97

rectangle
circle
hexagon
triangle
pentagon
octagon
kite
There are 20 triangles in the picture.

page 99

circle

triangle

rectangle

hexagon

page 101

sphere
cube
cone
pyramid
cylinder

The clown is made up of cubes, a sphere, a pyramid, cones and cylinders.

page 102

Parent to check colours of shapes.

cone

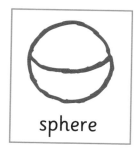

sphere

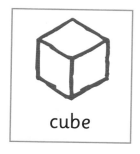

cube

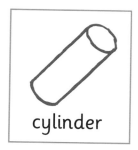

cylinder

page 103

cube

sphere

cuboid

pyramid

page 105

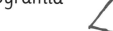

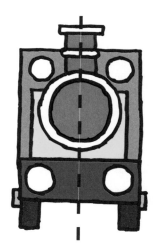

page 106

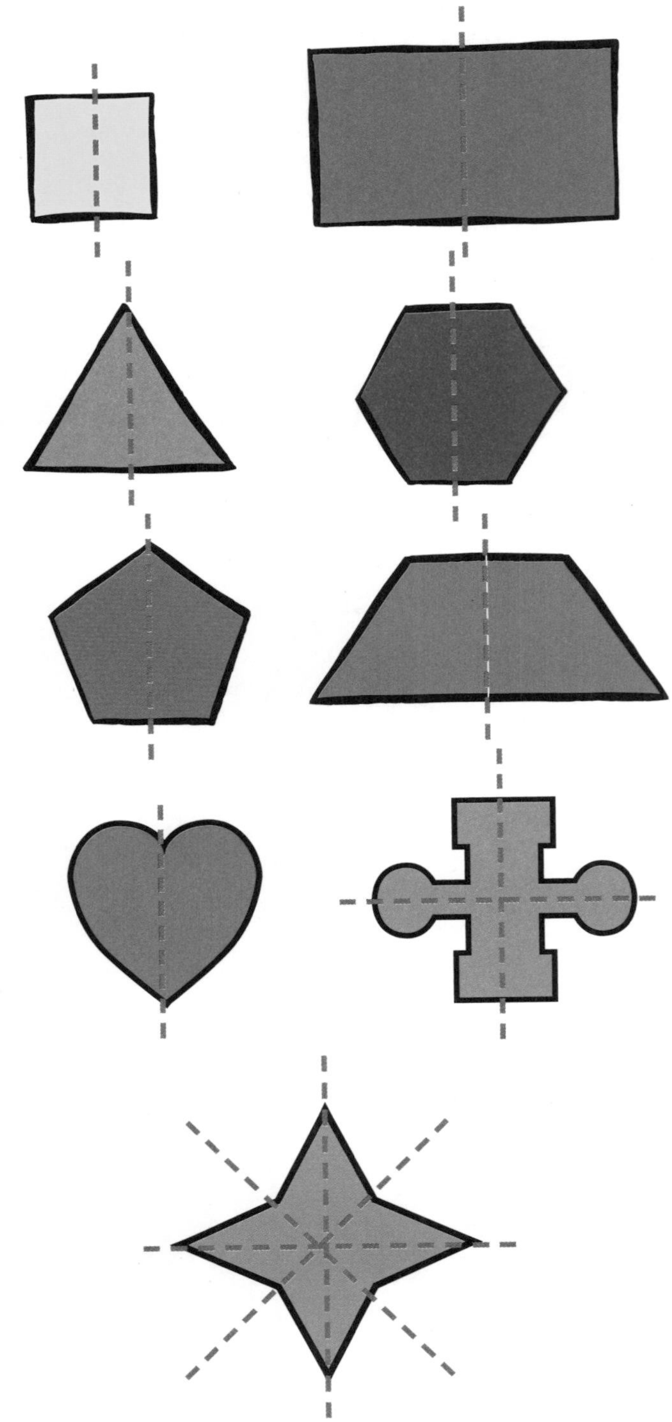

page 107

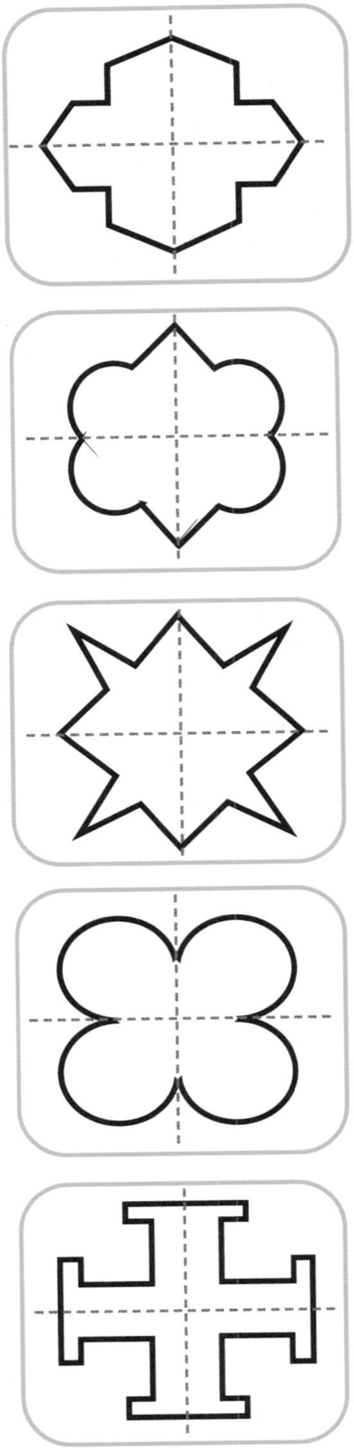

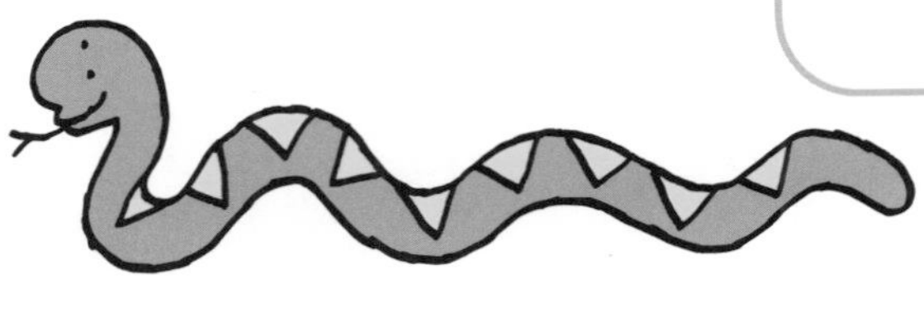

page 109

The biggest rocket is 7cm.
The smallest rocket is 3cm.

Parent to check sensible estimates.

 litre

 centimetre

page 110

blue — jug A
green — jug E
yellow — jug C
Jug E should be coloured in to the
2 pint mark.

The car is heavier than the dog.
The parcel weighs 4kg.

pencil — centimetres
bottle of pop — litres
strawberries — grams

 metre

 gram

page 111

3kg
8kg
5kg
2kg
4kg

page 112

A — 10cm
B — 15cm
C — 1cm
D — 6cm

The longest line is 15cm.
The shortest line is 1cm.
The difference in length between the
longest and shortest lines is 14cm.

page 113

A – 6cm
B – 13cm
C – 16cm
D – 3cm

The longest line is 16cm.
The shortest line is 3cm.
The difference in length between the longest and shortest lines is 13cm.

page 115

half-past 1
1:30

half-past 7
7:30

half-past 4
4:30

3 o'clock
3:00

1 o'clock
1:00

The party lasted 3 hours.

page 117

10 minutes to 4

3:50

10 minutes past 1

1:10

20 minutes past 4

4:20

20 minutes past 6

6:20

20 minutes past 8

8:20

page 118

1:45
12:15
3:40
4:50

11:27
8:50

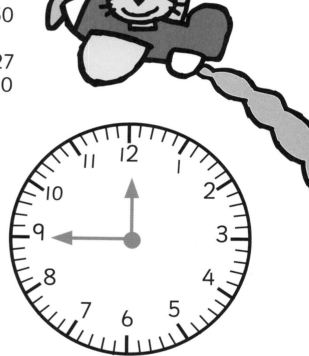

page 119

2:20
2:50
3:05
4:35
4:45

2D, two-dimensional

properties

corner, edge, surface, face

flat, curved

circle

triangle

square

rectangle

pentagon

hexagon

octagon

kite

3D, three-dimensional

solid, hollow

cube

cuboid

pyramid

sphere

cone

cylinder

☆

line of symmetry

mirror, reflection

☆

measure

length

centimetre (cm), metre (m)

estimate

weight

gram (g), kilogram (kg)

liquid

pint, litre

bigger, biggest

smaller, smallest

most, least

☆

time

seconds, minutes, hours, day

clock, watch, hands

o'clock, half-past, quarter-past,

quarter to, half an hour

start, finish

leave, arrive

digital, analogue

clock hand, short hand, long hand

After working through each section, put a tick in the box to show how you feel about the topic.

If you tick 'Not sure' go back to those pages and try again.

	Confident	Not sure
2D shapes		
3D shapes		
Symmetry		
Measuring		
Time		

Look out for
the companion title:
Mega English 5–7

Mega English 5–7
ISBN 978 1 4052 2013 2

**There are MEGA books
for younger children, too.
Look out for Maths 3–5
and English 3–5.**

Mega Maths 3–5
ISBN 978 1 4052 2012 5

Mega English 3–5
ISBN 978 1 4052 2011 8

Each book is packed with 128 pages of learning exercises
and 100 fun stickers to enjoy.

All titles comply with the National Curriculum (England and Wales)
and English and Mathematics 5–14 (Scotland) and are in line with the
Curriculum Guidance for the Foundation Stage, and the
National Literacy and Numeracy Strategies.

**These are the perfect books to help support your child's
progress through primary school.**